WE WERE MARINES

Walter F. Kling

We Were Marines

A Fictional Novel of Nine Marines
Who Gave Their All for
The Western Hemisphere,
Country, and Protectorates.
Their Justice for the Deadly
Criminals, Bandits, Insurgents,
And Terrorists was
Elimination.

For information
732-286-9714
WK

We Were Marines
For Corps and Country
To
Do or Die
Nine Marines
Believed the Monroe Doctrine
Of 1823
To Keep Out Foreign Intervention
In the Western Hemisphere
Protect our Protectorates
In the American Caribbean, Philippine Islands, Nicaragua
And To
"Deep Six"
The Corruptors of the American and
Native American People
The Criminals, Bandits, Insurgents, and
Hostile Irregulars

My special thanks to my wife Stephanie
and our friend Eileen Conrad
a great supporting team.

Printed by: Trec

Published by Walter F. Kling and Trec

We Were Marines
PO BOX 3055
Holiday City 730 Jamaica Blvd.
Toms River, NJ. 08756-3055

Printed in the United States of America

We Were Marines

who believed
The Monroe Doctrine of 1823
opposed
to European Countries on intervention
in the Americas
The United Stated of America
had
the right to help stabilize
the
Caribbean and Central American Countries
and
protect our possessions and protectorates in
the Atlantic and Pacific Ocean
Areas and Islands.

It
Has Been Said
History
Repeats Itself

Keep Out Of Foreign Entanglements
When Involved
Deep Six Your Enemies
The Killers, Bandits, Insurgents, Terrorists
Will Always Come Back Sooner
Or later to
Kill You or Your Children

History
Politicians, Judges, and Juries
Who Betray You Were
Tarred and Feathered

This has Been Going on Since
Time Began and May
Never End
UNTIL
The End of Time
And Now

We Were Marines

We Were Marines

For
God, Corps, and Country
Respect, Honor, Protect

Introducing
Cast of Characters
Special Force ILRP (*)

Marines
Major John Smith (*)
Lieutenant P.H. Dell Rico (*)
Lieutenant H.J. Byrnes (*)
Sergeant Walter F. Kling (*)
Sergeant Edward J. Pikus (*)
Corporal H.G. Wells (*)
Corporal R.C. Zeke (*)
Private First Class Charles Sambach (*)
Private First Class Frank Eckert (*)
Colonel W. Quick
Major T. Johnson
Major H. Bean
Captain S. Bryla
Captain J. Conrad

And

United States Coast Guard
Lieutenant Frank E. Kling

United States Navy
Gunner's Mate Louis J. Byrnes

We Were Marines

This Book Is Dedicated to:

United States Marines

Charles Sambach (D)	World War I
Frank Eckert (D)	World War I
Walter F. Kling	World War II
Richard Eckert (D)	Korean Era
Robert Eckert	Korean Era
William Eckert (Marines/ Navy) (D)	Korean Era
George Katzenberger	Korean Era
Walter Stockinger (D)	Vietnam
John Grabowski (D)	World War II
Alfred Timinski (D)	World War II
Timothy Timinski	Korean Era
Stanley Bryla	World War II

United States Coast Guard

Frank E. Kling	World War II

United States Navy

Louis J. Byrnes	World War II

Author's Note: all of the above are related.
(D): deceased

About The Author

The author, Walter F. Kling, was born in New Jersey. He is ninety years of age, married 65 years to the same woman and no stranger to Ocean County, where he owned a business and property for many years. He worked in the food and appliance industry, Forestry Service in Montana, and detective agencies in New Jersey. In World War II, he was enlisted as a regular Marine from 1942 to 1946. After two years overseas, in the Caribbean areas, he returned to the United States to retrain for the Pacific. Due to training in the field, his features, face and head were defaced. Slightly blinded, he remained at Quantico, Virginia, Officers Training Area, Marine Corps Schools. He completed studies in criminology and fingerprint identification at the Marine Corps Institute. Previous studies were in fingerprints at Boston School of Criminology. Awards – Granted the designation of Registered Criminologist – 1963. He was a forerunner and worked in hospital security, safety and identification of personnel and also Security Director Association. Kling is a Charter Life Member of the Marine Corps Association, the Marine Corps League at Large, Det, ML and the Toms River Elk 1875, and a licensed private detective for 27 years.

Chapter I

I was born March 2, 1875 in Orange, New Jersey. After what schooling I could get I told my parents I was going to enlist in the United States Marines. I was seventeen years of age. My father was a Marine in the Civil War and wounded in the left shoulder. I was told I would have to go to New York City to enlist.

I found the enlistment offices for Army, Navy, and Marines on the second floor of the Post Office building on Vesey Street. I went into the Marine office to enlist.

A Marine Sergeant said he would explain the procedure. After signing papers, I was told to go into the next room where a Navy doctor was going to make a complete examination of my body. While waiting to be examined I met a fellow by the name of Ed Pikus. We both passed our examinations and were told to stand by to be sworn in. We were now U.S. Marines.

The Marine Sergeant said we would be shipped to a new Marine recruit depot at Parris Island, South Carolina near Port Royal sound. We would go by train to Beaufort, South Carolina and then by horse and wagon to the depot. Actually, we were in a convoy of horses and wagons loaded with building materials, tents, weapons, food clothing, and twenty more recruits. Marines have been trained at Washington, D.C., Philadelphia, Pa., Quantico, Virginia, and key West, Florida. Some were also trained on battle wagons.

They traveled through swamps over what was called a road with holes, bushes, and a million mosquitoes until we reached a long flat track of sandy land not too far from the water. We were told this was a trial area to see if it was a good place for a Marine Training Depot and then later on a base. "O Happy Day!"

Twenty-two of us recruits would train here and be used as work men. It was now 0900 hours. An advance party of Marine NCO'S and Privates had already erected two and four man tents. Water lines were run from a wooden wagon tank.

Rubber bags were on poles in the tent areas. Out houses called heads, wash tents, as well as a mess tent, first aid, and administration tent were also erected.

A sergeant and two corporals told us recruits to form a straight line. The sergeant asked if we knew our left from our right side. We all laughed and said, "Yes Sir". The corporal showed us how to make a right and left face, and where our arms and legs should be at the position of attention. Always start with the left foot when marching. After one hour of this the sergeant called us to attention. He said we would be taught the manual of arms later. We then were marched to the first aid tent where we had a body examination and given needles into the arm, also short arm inspection.

At the Fresh Air Barbershop all hair on our head was cut off including mustaches. Next we were marched to the administration tent where a lieutenant gave us a full explanation of rules and regulations, discipline and duty. First he said we should be obedient to orders, show good behavior, fighting spirit, reliability, loyalty, courage, truthfulness, honor, and have self control. He also said moral turpitude, refusal to obey, neglect of duty, intoxication, desertion, thefts, misconduct, fighting, and disturbances would be punishable by a Deck Court, Summary Court, or General Court Martial. He also said, "Do not get any tattooing on your body. It marks you for life". Our pay would be twelve dollars a month. Government insurance may be available. He also explained saluting and furloughs.

A penal platoon of thirty Marines were now being punished at this depot under the supervision of Marine Engineers and M.P. Guards. They will build a rifle range, barracks, and clear swamps. We were not to acknowledge them. Their tent areas were under armed guard twenty-four hours a day. The only privileges they were allowed were for food, work, drilling, silence, and sleep.

The lieutenant then turned us over to a first sergeant who gave us our first training schedule. We then went for clothing and gear issue.

Training: First Seven Days for New Recruits
(after two days of orientation)

Reveille 0500

Head and Wash 0530

Roll Call 0531 – 0540

Exercise 0545 – 0615

Police Call 0616 – 0655
clean tent area, make cots

First Mess Call 0700 – 0800
breakfast

Head Call 0801 – 0830
bathroom

Troop and Drill 0831 – 1031
Manual of arms

Work Assignments 1036 – 1300

Lunch Call 1300- 1400

Clothes 1401 – 1500
clothes marking

Bayonet Practice 1502 – 1600

Return to Tents 1601 – 1725
wash and clean rifles

Mess Call 1730 – 1845

Return to Tents 1900
free time 1930 – 2130
tattoo 2140 – 2159

Taps 2200
lamps out

Night Guards on Duty 2200 – 0500
three lamps in each tent row

Marine Issued Clothing

1 campaign hat with Marine emblem
1 dress blue hat
1 dress blue blouse with emblems
1 pair dress blue trousers
2 khaki shirts
2 khaki ties
2 khaki summer trousers
2 pair khaki leggings
3 pair white socks
2 pair heavy woolen socks
2 khaki belts
1 garrison belt 3 ½ inches, black
2 pair work& drill & trousers
2 pair work & drill blouses – jackets
2 woolen blankets –
1 sea bag
1 pair work & drill shoes
1 pair dress shoes

Marine Issued 782 Gear

1 Krag-Jorgensen -30-40 cal.
1 U.S. Bayonet
1 first aid pouch
1 canteen & cover
1 mess kit – knife, fork, spoon
1 shelter half – 3 pegs
1 cartridge belt – 90 rounds
(90 rounds -30-4- cartridges)
1 poncho, mattress, pillow, sheets

We were also issued a tooth brush, paste, small mirror, razor, shaving brush and soap. Also a brush, clothes and body soap. A three gallon water pail was added. The Sergeant said we would be charged six dollars to pay for these items. It would come out of our first month's pay.

Thirty-eight recruits joined us; in all there were now sixty recruits to train in this hell hole of swamps, mosquitos, sand fleas, and flies.

Our second day of orientation started a Reveille 0500. Head, wash, cots, and policing, drill clothes uniform of the day, field shoes, and then mess call 0700. After morning mess we were marched to the supply tent where ID tags were issued. Two hours of drill, orientation, and history of the corps – Do or Die. After noon mess we were finger printed. 1430 orientation was our training program for the next four and a half months. The corporals and sergeants had the daily schedules and times. The training program consisted of : Inspection and Drill, Manual of Arms-daily, bayonet, cutlass, knife fighting, defend, fighting with the arms and legs, boxing, death dealing blows, knife and hatchet , throwing hand and trench grenades, instructions and rifle firing

> 30-40 Krag-Jorgensen Rifle
> 303 Lee – 1889
> 45-70 Springfield Rifle
> 45 & 38 Revolvers
> 1883 – Gatling machine gun
> Colt automatic machine gun
> Hotchkiss canon

We had to familiarize ourselves with all the above weapons. We continued the schedule of firing the Krag-Jorgenses, 303 Lee rifles, and 38 special revolvers until the whole platoon qualified as marksmen.

Ed Pikus and I made expert with the rifles and revolvers. Three quarters of the platoon made sharpshooters.

We also had training on beach landings from whale boats and training on the infantry pack, compass flag kit, general orders, use of cover, hand combat signals, skirmishes, methods of attack, mopping up, flank security, the platoon in defense, scouting, deployment, horse and mule care. Swimming was added to the schedule. Chewing, smoking tobacco was not allowed during training by recruits or training personnel.

Depot personnel were allowed to smoke only at free time.

Well, the training time went by fast but the mosquitoes, sand fleas, and flies almost drove us crazy. We were issued mosquito nets. The water in the wagon tanks was bad. Trying to keep clean was a problem and I swear I saw worms in the stews.

Two of the sergeants and corporals of the platoon took a shine to Ed and me. We had the best records of the whole training platoon. The discipline was murderous and most training was done on the double. Ed and I with ten other Marines were being assigned to the barracks at Norfolk, Virginia for base security. We did gate and base security.

Since Ed and I qualified with the .45 and .38 cal. Revolvers and made expert on the Krag-Jorgensen rifle, 1889 Mauser 98 and the 1889 Lee-Enfield rifles the base marine captain called us into his office and said we both would be instructors on the base and rifle range from 0730 to 1400 daily Monday through Friday, guard, MP in Norfolk on Saturdays and Sunday off. Some fun!

Ed and I had two years and five months at Norfolk. We were promoted to corporals. We asked the captain for a change of stations and he said he could transfer us to a new training battalion now forming in Quantico, Virginia. After a year in the training battalion Ed and I were promoted to Buck Sergeants and transferred back to Norfolk, Virginia marine Barracks where we were in charge of the rifle range again.

1898 the United States was having trouble with Spain. Our captain told us to pick up our gear and get over to the USS Texas now in port. At last sea going marines! So we thought. Ninety other marines were transferred to the battleship USS Texas. We had a major, first sergeant, platoon sergeant, six corporals, and us two buck sergeants all new to seagoing. Ed and I were no sooner on board the Texas and assigned our quarters when a marine orderly appeared at the hatchway and told us we were to report to Major Smith immediately. The orderly had us follow him to the Major's quarters. The Major's door was open we walked in. Marines do not salute uncovered. The Major said to sit down and give him our full attention. He said he had our record books and was impressed. He looked us straight in the eyes and said he had two special missions that he believed we were the Marines to accomplish them. "First" he said, "I will assign one corporal and four first class privates to each of you. You people will be quartered all twelve to one large room on the ship. You will all eat together, and sleep in cots. You shall not talk to any of the crew or other Marines on board. Your training in the large quarters will last ten days. The only people you shall have contact with are myself, Lieutenant Dell Rico a Philippine Marine who is a knife thrower and fighter and Lieutenant Lew Byrnes. They will teach you the tricks of our trade. To Kill. Lieutenant Byrnes shall school you on field sanitation, how to draw maps read a compass, how to handle all gear, food, ammunition, and how to kill quietly. He will also teach you when and only when to use grenades on this trip. You people will also have target practice on the stern of the ship. Rifles and revolvers no audience, restricted area only. Lieutenant Byrnes will give you some schooling on how to speak Spanish and first aid. You will also receive instructions on bullet wounds. He then told us to turn over our seabags and all winter gear to the supply sergeant. A bag was issued for our summer wear.

The USS Texas set sail at 2100 hours February 2, 1898. Out in the Atlantic we met a convoy of four destroyers, one coaler, one supply ship, and one target ship. The target ship had whale boats and rubber rafts. While the navy had target practice we continued with our schooling and training. We had been sailing around the south Atlantic now about thirteen days. On Feb. 15 the USS Battleship Maine was sunk in a Cuban harbor. Two hundred and sixty Americans were lost. On February 16 the Major called the two Lieutenants and the twelve of us to his quarters. He said we would be going on a special mission in the Caribbean. Ed Pikus and I would be landing at Ensenda Honda, Puerto LeCondo. Lt. Del Rico and twenty Marines would be landed on Crab Island to destroy any Spanish radios or telegraph stations and personnel. My mission would be to travel west on the island of Puerto le Condo and map any interior military bases, equipment, artillery, and man power. Ed Pikus and his five men would travel east with the same instructions. We would be landing at night and given four days to secure the information. One of the Texas' whale boats would land us and pick us up at midnight on the fourth day.

I had with me Corporal Zeke, Privates Oscar Livera, Brucie Wells, Mike Saprano, and Dickie Johnson. We traveled as near to the shore as we could by a town named Farjardo. We were about fifteen miles from where we landed. We only spotted one radio and telegraph station with about fifty Spanish soldiers hanging around. Four or five houses and a house of prostitution made up the area. Brucie Boy Wells wanted to go into the house he said the girls wouldn't know the difference. He spoke Spanish and he was crazy anyway. We saw ten bicycles parked in back of the telegraph office, no one was around so we took off. The next thing I thought of was to get six Spanish uniforms. Then we could travel with ease. Three of my men spoke Spanish. We traveled up the road to Vena Cava a town of about five hundred people mostly fishermen and farmers. Outside of this town there were about two hundred tents with clothes hanging on the tent lines. Spanish uniforms, o' boy we were in. "Now you will see how six raggedy assed Marines work ." I told Zeke and Mike to go up trail for about a half a mile do some shooting and then return immediately. The shooting was a diversion so we could steal the uniforms and clothes. Brucie Boy, Dickie, and I rolled along the ground toward the tents. The diversion caused just about all the noise I expected. People and Spanish soldiers started up the road and trail leaving very few guards. We grabbed all the uniforms we could hold and raced back to our position in the jungle. Zeke and Mike returned about twenty-five minutes later. Talk about luck No one saw us. We dressed in the ill fitting uniforms as best we could. We were a sad sight as Spanish soldiers. By bicycles we set out for the Spanish base at Ponce about forty miles west. We passed soldiers and police with our full equipment and no one stopped us or talked to us. They just nodded their heads and we nodded back and waved. "Some luck!"

We had to bury some food and equipment back where we changed uniforms. At Vena Cava no tobacco of any kind was used on this trip. We left the jungle and then returned to the road traveling toward our destination Ponce. As we traveled some people passed us and waved. We bicycled around a sharp curve about a half mile toward Ponce when we ran smack into a road block. A Spanish sergeant and two privates walked toward us. I touched my knife which was a signal to my men to get off their bikes and dispatch the three soldiers which they did quickly. We dragged the bodies off the road near the edge of the jungle and then retreated back into the jungle about a quarter of a mile overlooking the Ponce Military Base.

Each of us was wearing a ragged Spanish uniform, carrying a Krag-Jorgensen rifle, .38 cal revolver, 2 trench hand grenades, and ninety rounds of ammunition for the rifle and fifty rounds for the revolvers plus a small first aid kit, canteen of water, bayonet, and knife. We also had some rope, dynamite, fuses, and caps.

While walking on a trail through the jungle with the bicycles a male person approached us and said, "American?" Brucie Boy spoke to him in Spanish. This guy said he was looking for us. He was a member of the Rebel Puerto LeCondos. Some civilians along the road figured out we were Americans by the way we traveled. He was happy he found us. His name was Joe. Joe said about two hundred rebels were way back in the jungles waiting to attack the base and cause trouble for the Spanish. They planned to kill them, set fires, destroy everything they could. Brucie Boy asked Joe to take us to them. We met up with the rebels and talked to their captain, Juan. He spoke English and said he would help us get all the desired information to take back to our commanding officer and then he would attack. I told him we did not want the Spanish to know that Americans were in the area at this time.

Brucie Boy. Mike, and Dickie joined twenty rebels and were able to walk all around the Ponce base because they spoke Spanish. No one challenged them. Brucie Boy said there was no organization or discipline. Joe said he believed they all suffered from dipsomania. The Spanish had a building loaded with thousands of rounds of all type of ammunition, rifles, pistols, and artillery. Captain Juan said he would destroy it all after we departed.

One thing people should know about the Marines Code –Do or Die Kill or be Killed. Your ass belongs to your God and country. No retreat, no surrender. One other thing – when a Marine is in combat or skirmish he may have trouble with his bowels, some Marines don't evacuate their bowels for days. Marines can't wash or brush their teeth there is no water sometimes, and they sometimes end up with scabies. The peaches and cream only comes when the Army and Navy looks at heaven scenes. They will find the streets are guarded by United States Marines.

We bicycled back toward Farjardo forty miles to the east where we landed. I decided to change uniforms at Vena Cave. It was time to get rid of the dirty Spanish uniforms and get into our khakis. We made the change and buried the Spanish uniforms. We continued riding our bikes down the road to the town entrance where we were challenged at a road block that was not there on our way up to Ponce. Ten Spanish soldiers and one sergeant. Two Spanish soldiers were behind a Gatling machine gun and the rest were pointing their rifles toward us. Dickie Johnson and Mike Saprano without hesitation threw two trench grenades. One landed on the Gatling gun exploding and knocking down five men. The other grenade knocked down the other four men. Zeke shot the sergeant and one man trying to get away. All the Spanish soldiers were shot by Brucie Boy Wells. We were not to be identified as Americans in the area so we cut off the sergeant's head and penis and some of the soldier's penises and stuffed them in their mouths. We wanted the Spanish officers to believe the rebels knocked out the road block. We checked to make sure we didn't leave anything and then took off for Farjardo.

On the outskirts of Farjardo we ran in to sniper fire. Oscar Livera was shot through the head and Dickie Johnson was shot through the stomach. Both men died instantly. I yelled to take cover. We did not spot the sniper at first but Brucie Boy saw him in a tree and fired two shots killing him. We had about fifteen mile to go. I carried Dickie Johnson and Zeke carried Oscar Livera. We could not leave their bodies in this area. Brucie boy kept one bike which he loaded with rifles, knap sacks, ammunitions, and a few other things. We had to bury some of our equipment. We carried Dickie and Oscar for about a mile then we did the best we could with burying them in the jungle. I marked the area on my map. That's one price of glory-death.

We made it back to where we landed three hours before the pickup time. Ed Pikus was there waiting for us. He lost five men and all his equipment. He was lucky to be alive. A bullet sliced his right arm. He did manage to get the desired information. Ed said when he headed east with his men he traveled about ten mile toward Fort DeSoto and San Jose when he met up with two hundred fifty rebels who said they were going to attack Fort DeSoto. Those rebels wanted blood. They hated the Spanish soldiers. They were led by foolish rebel officers.

Fort DeSoto had coast artillery, field artillery, and forty Gatling machine guns as well as three battle ships off the coast and about three thousand Spanish sailors, marines, and soldiers.

I had the information and started back with my men then the rebels attacked. What slaughter! Unknown to the rebels one thousand Spanish soldiers were transferred from Ponce to Fort DeSoto. They had the rebels surrounded and they killed my five men before they could fire a shot. The rebel soldiers who tried to surrender were shot. This was no place for me so I went deeper into the jungles and headed west for our landing area. I had no trouble getting back. Ed and I got back to the Texas and reported to Major Smith who was happy with our reports but not happy with losing seven Marines.

The Texas and support ships sailed around the Caribbean area and met a larger convoy of American ships. On board the Texas we learned all the ship's lingo and were trained on what the navy called a forty inch gun. Lt. Dell Rico was back on board and the Spanish lessons started up again. Lt. Dell Rico said he had no trouble on Crab Island there were ten Spanish sailors and a telegraph station.

On April 24, 1898 the United States declared war on Spain. We were now sailing in the Caribbean Sea off Mayoquez, Puerto LeCondo. The Battleships Maryland and Arizona joined us along with the cruisers Atlanta, Minneapolis, and Indianapolis. The destroyers numbered about ten with two supply ships, two coal ships, and one transport the USS Merrill. There were one thousand Marines on the Merrill ready for combat.

Major Smith called us to his quarters and asked if Ed, Zeke, Brucie Boy, Mike, and I would like to be in the lead platoon in the landing and invasion of Mayoquez and Ponce, Puerto LeCondo.

Well we landed June 14, 1898 and had our part of the island secured by July 15th. The Army had their part secured by July 17th. Teddy Roosevelt and his Rough Riders and the Army secured Cuba. We had the south Atlantic and Caribbean islands secured. The Spanish American War ended July 25, 1898.

Chapter 2

On August 26, 1898 Major Smith called us to his quarters. He said the Navy Department in Washington, D.C. was communicating with the Texas radio room and sent the following message for him. Promotions: Major Smith to Lieutenant Colonel, Lt. Dell Rico to Captain, Lt. Byrnes to Captain, Sergeant Walter F. Kling to First Sergeant, Sgt. Ed Pikus to Gunnery Sgt., Corporal Bob Zeke to Staff Sgt., Pfc. Brucie Wells to Sgt., Pfc. Mike Saprano to Sgt. transferred to USS. Arizona. August 30, 1898 three Marine officers and five enlisted Marines mentioned above were transferred by whale boat 1500 hours August 30, 1898-WDN-Admiral John Stone paper work to follow.

Lt. Colonel Smith asked the Captain of the Texas if he could have a party in his quarters and serve wine, beer, and steaks to his two new captains and five sergeants. Permission was granted. Colonel Smith said how happy he was to serve with us and we would get together on the Arizona and find out our destinations.

We made the trip to the USS. Arizona arriving at 1530 hours and received congratulations from the Arizona's Captain on our promotions, a Marine Guard of Honor – "Does it get any better!" There were two hundred Marines on the ship. After we were assigned our quarters Colonel Smith called the seven of us to meet in the Ready Room. He told us we were sailing to the Pacific, down the south Atlantic around the Cape Horn to Santiago, Chile then to San Diego, California where we would get ten days furlough. Most of the men said they were going to get a girl, a good steak, and then a hotel room. Ed and I decided to go hunting and fishing up in the Serra Mountains. We went to the downtown hunting club in San Diego where we met two females who were looking for guides or males to go hunting with. "Again, does it get any better?"

Now, these two females were in their thirties, both had husbands that were dead. One woman told me she lost her husband on a hunting trip. He fell off a cliff. The other woman said her husband drowned while fishing. "Talk about spoon tang."

At the hunting club we met a man and his wife who said they owned two cabins in the Sierra's near Tahoe, it would take about a day and a half to get there but that it would be worth the trip. They wanted forty dollars rent for the large cabin for five days. We could get all the supplies we needed at the general store, including renting rifles and fishing gear. The cabin was only a mile from the general store in Tahoe. A day and a half trip up and back and five days at the cabin we could be back to the Arizona on time with two days to spare. "What a hunting trip!" The girl I paired with was named Betty Rich. Ed's girlfriend's name was Ann Grey. The girls understood men's needs and fell all over two twenty-five year old marines. Betty shot a ten point deer and I ended up with a twelve pointer. Ed shot a five hundred pound black bear and Ann shot a fifteen point Mule Tail deer. We kept some of the steaks of the animals and gave the skin and meat to the local inhabitants.

Betty and Ann said they were nurses at Saint Mary's hospital in National City where they resided. One of the things I found out during the trip was that Ed had a brother in the Marines and that his father was a marine in the Civil War. We took the girls to their homes and told them the next time we were in port we would see them. "Boy, what kisses good-bye!"

We went back to San Diego, rented a hotel room got drunk for one day and then returned to the Arizona.

We were in our quarters at 0930 hours when a Chief Petty Officer told us to report to Colonel Smith in the Officer's Ready two amid ship on the u upper deck. Colonel Smith was called back to the ship earlier from his leave the Colonel said to round up Sergeants Bob Zeke, Brucie Wells, Mike Saprano, and a Petty Officer Corpsman named John Cole. We were to report back to him in Ready Room two at 1400 hours. The Colonel said the men he named should be on this ship and he put me in charge. I had all the men he wanted to see in Ready

Room two at 1400 hours.

The Colonel warmly greeted us and said he wanted disciplined volunteer marines who spoke, understood, or had knowledge of the Moro Spanish dialects of the Philippine Islands. He also wanted Marines who had knowledge of the Cantonese dialects of the Chinese. Colonel Smith said he knew it was a large order with only about 3,500 men in the corps at this time and that it would be impossible to get qualified volunteers. However, he would select any qualified volunteer enlisted Navy men. This in all would be a special platoon of sixty men. I knew some of the cooks and mess boys in the Navy spoke the Philippine language and island dialects. "Some people will not return from this special assignment. I am open for volunteers."

Sgt. Kling – yes
Sgt. Pikus – yes
Sgt. Zeke – yes
Sgt. Wells – yes
Sgt. Saprano – yes
Chief Petty Officer Cole – yes
Captains Dell Rico and Byrnes have already volunteered.

"You people will be the cream of the crop and will report to marine Barracks San Diego building H02. Captains Dell Rico and Byrnes will be there to greet you. They shall pass out your written assignments as well tell you confidential information. You people are not to talk to any base personnel about your duties. You will have special passes to come and go off base and acquire duty information. Marine and Navy personnel shall cooperate."

The nine of us will select and train fifty-one men. January 3, 1901 Marine Barracks Training Center San Diego building H02 NCO quarters Captain Dell Rico told the six of us the special platoon would only have three months training and then we would be on our way to the Philippine islands. I was to contact personnel headquarters San Diego area for qualified volunteer Marines from ships or other areas where

Marines were assigned west of the Rocky Mountains.

Ed Pikus was assigned to go to the Armory marine Barracks San Diego to select all the equipment on his list. Pistols, rifles, automatic weapons, grenades, ammunition all to be delivered to building H02 when notified. Sgt. Zeke was assigned to order the clothing we would need and transportation, forage, and subsistence from the Quartermaster Marine Barracks, San Diego. Sergeants Wells and Saprano would interview the men reporting and select the qualified volunteers. The men selected would be told, "This is a fifty fifty deal. You may not return. If selected, you are sworn to secrecy and cannot tell what your duty is. You may have to kill in cold blood, destroy property, shoot women, children, and old people, or torture the enemy. The mission is dealing with some very cruel people. They are not merciful."

Building H02 was one of the new sixty men barracks with double metal bunks, NCO quarters, office, an Orderly room, and an inside was and shower room with a head - a twelve seater flush toilets. There was a three stall NCO and Officer's head, washroom, and shower.

January 5, 1901 0900 hours Colonel Smith called the eight of us together. He said he wanted to tell us what personnel were needed for the special platoon. First he said, "Navy Chief Petty Officer Cole. " Cole had twelve years experience in the navy as a corpsman, pharmacist, mate, and participated in many medical operations. "He is no stranger in the operating room and has treated many wounds." We would need five corpsmen with at least two years experience. Nine signal flag men with lantern experience, five Navy men (sailors) who could speak and understand the Moro and Philippine dialects. Twenty navy men and thirty Marines, Corporals or PFC's who could speak and understand the Spanish language with at least two years service. Four of the Marines had to have experience and could operate the Colt automatic machine gun or any machine guns now in service.

Table of organization

NCO's and Officers in charge
Commanding Officer Colonel J Smith
Aide de Camp Captains Dell Rico and Byrnes

1st Squad	2nd Squad
Ms Sgt. WF Kling	First Sgt. Pikus
1-Corporal - Marine	1-Corporal - Marine
2-Navy signalmen	2-Navy signalmen
1-Corpsman – Navy	1-Corspman - Navy
2-Spanish speaking sailors	2-Spanish speaking sailors
1-Marine machine gun	1-Marine machine gun
5-Marine – riflemen	5-Marine – riflemen

3rd Squad	4th Squad
Sgt. Zeke	Sgt. Wells
1-Corporal – Marine	1-Corporal - Marine
2-Navy signalmen	2-Navy signalmen
1-Corspman – Navy	1-Corpsman - Navy
2-Spanish speaking sailors	2-Spanish speaking sailors
1-Marine machine gun	1-Marine machine gun
5-Marine – riflemen	5-Marine – riflemen

Table of Organization

Reserve
Sgt. M. Saprano
Chief Petty Officer Cole – Medical
1-Marine – rifleman
1-Bugler – Marine
1-Navy signalman

Marine and Navy personnel by name and serial number
to be assigned by Captain Byrnes

"By January 18 this platoon shall be formed to start training. Captain Dell Rico shall have everyman selected for special platoon, medically examined, and inoculated. Base Mess Hall number 3 will serve our food. Breakfast-lunch-dinner at the appropriate hours. "

January 20, 1891 0930 hours Colonel Smith called together all the men of the special platoon in Barrack H02. he said he would tell us the general rules.

1.Discipline
2.Refusal to obey
3.Misconduct – thefts
4.Neglect of duty
5.Unauthorized absence
6.Moral turpitude
7.Gambling
8.Smoking while on duty or patrol
9.intoxication
10.Desertion
11.Fighting or disturbances
12.Loyalty – Reliability – Honesty

Violations shall bring severe penalties.

"Captain Byrnes today at 1300 hours will give you a talk on what I just enumerated as well as inspection, marking of your clothing and gear, deposits of your money, insurance, haircuts, and other pertinent advice.

Platoon Personnel Schedule:
    Reveille 0530hr
    Fall out-Roll call exercises 0550 – 0620hr
    Personal hygiene, make bunks 0630 – 0655hr
    Mess call 0700 – 0800hr
    Police call, clean barracks 0805 – 0835hr
    Troop and Drill –Manual of Arms 0840- 0950hr

First week training-Monday to Saturday;

Rifle, pistol selection and issue   1000 – 1200hr
Rifle and pistol cleaning, inspection
Sighting, position, aiming drill –windage elevation-safety precautions
Mess call 1205 – 1300hr
Knife and bayonet fighting 1315 – 1415hr
First aid
Hand and trench grenades 1415 – 1450hr
Rifle and pistol dry firing practice 1450 – 1550 hr
Loop and hasty sling adjustment
Hand and flag signals 1555 – 1635hr
Rifle and weapons clean 1640 – 1750hr
Evening mess 1800 – 1930hr
Free time at barracks 1930 – 2145hr
Tattoo 2145hr
Lights out Taps 2200hr

Saturday: 0830 – 1205hr
Rifle and pistol range – live firing
Rifle positions and firing
Standing 100 yd 25 rounds
Sitting 200 yd 25 rounds
Kneeling 200 yd 25 rounds
Prone 300 yd 25 rounds
Mess call 1215 – 1305hr
Pistol range;1310 – 1430
10 yd 6 rounds
25 yd 6 rounds
50 yd 6 rounds
Wash clothes 1435 – 1635hr
Free time 1635 – 1800hr
Mess call 1800 – 1930hr
Free time 1935 – 2145hr
Tattoo 2145hr
Taps 2200hr

Sunday – Free Day

January 22, Ed Pikus came down with malaria. Sgt. Kling had to take over the first and second squads for four days. Captain Dell Rico told Kling to tell the troops that a pay increase had been granted by Congress: Private $24.00 monthly, PFC $30.00, Corporal $36.00, Sergeant $42.00 monthly, Staff Sergeants $48.00, First sergeant and Gunnery Sergeant $60.00, Master Sergeant $75.00, all commissioned officers a twenty-two percent increase.

February 3, 1901 to March 3, 1901 we completed all forms of training, jungle fighting, and everyone qualified with the rifles and pistols. Each man was told how to live off the land-what to eat.

March 15, 1901 we were told to pack up we would board the Battleship Maryland docked San Diego at 1300 hours on March 18, 1901. The Battleship Maryland was joined by one coal ship, two cruiser, The Wichta Houston, and six destroyers. Each ship had thirty marines on board. Marine units on each ship had one machine gun, two 60 mortars, and twenty-four of the new type hand grenades.

Our ship stopped at Pearl Harbor, Hawaii for supplies, coal, and water. Colonel Smith called us together and said, "Next stop Manila on the Philippine island of Luzon."

The Army had been chasing the insurgents around for one year. They were trying to catch the leader Emilio Aquinalde but, he would move from Luzon to Panay, Palawan, and Mindoro. The Army now believed they had him with five hundred insurgents located on Luzon. Our job for the special unit was to capture Emilio dead or alive, to destroy all the insurgents, and bring peace to the area.

In Manila First Sgt. Pikus and his twelve man team would board and be landed at Aparri in the northern end of Luzon. He would work his way south toward manila. The Destroyer Porter would also land fifteen Marines with Pikus for security which included one machine gun and a mortar team. The Destroyer would patrol the area for signals from Pikus. Sgt. Wells's special team with the same to as Pikus would be landed at San Fernando and work his way west to meet up with Pikus. His contact Destroyer Jones would patrol the coastal areas for signals. Sgt. Zeke would be landed at San H Defonzo and work his way east to meet Sgt. Wells' patrol. The Destroyer Cole would patrol the areas for signals. Sgt. Kling and his special team with thirty Marines would head north from Manila to meet Pikus, Wells, and Zeke. A search and destroy mission. The Army would put units all over other islands of the Philippines.

0900 hours April 5, 1901 Ed Pikus, his special team and fifteen marines were landed on the east coast near Apari, Luzon. Pikus marched his teams and supplies inland about a mile from the coast and set a perimeter around a hill. He set his machine gun team facing the thickest part of the jungle and spread his men out in teams of two. At 1400 hours sniper fire came in at him from the jungle. One of his Marines was wounded in the right arm. Unknown to Pikus at this time he had landed in a viper's nest of one hundred and fifty insurgents. At 1430 hours the insurgents attacked. Pikus and his machine gun teams surprised them. Twenty were killed within minutes. They were running away in a wave from the thickest part of the jungle. Pikus' flag team notified the Destroyer porter. Two of his men received minor wounds.

On April 6, the next day at 0600 hours Pikus with twenty Marines went hunting insurgents. The Destroyer Porter after hearing of the attack on Pikus landed fifteen more Marines at 0100 to support Pikus. Those bastard insurgents did not know Sgt. Ed Pikus. Pikus had his machine gun team, one mortar man with 10 rounds of 60mm, and seventeen Marine to hunt with.

Five miles on the west side of Apari Pikus found their camp and Pikus and the Marines disposed of the guards and lookouts. At a fast count one hundred insurgents were eating, washing, fooling around. Pikus had his mortar man drop one 60mm round in the middle of the camp, one on the east side, and one on the west side. His machine gun went into action plus his riflemen. It was a slaughter. Pikus had his men kill all the wounded. Ninety-five men and boys were killed and five women. The rest of the insurgents ran into the jungle. Pikus had the mortar man drop one more round where they ran and killed six more. "War is hell!" Who said that?

Pikus now had five men wounded and they were returned to the destroyer. Pikus decided on two days rest for his men then they would continue south killing snipers and pushing the insurgents toward Zeke, Wells, and Kling.

Sgt. Wells landed at San Fernando at 0930 hours and started working his way west. He came to a small barrio and could not believe his eyes. Five men and three women were crucified on rude crosses. The men had their private parts stuffed in their mouths and the women were cut open their guts hanging out. Twenty-five men and women came out of the jungle and offered their services as trackers, runners, or whatever they could do to avenge what had happened to their barrio. Wells' Marines were infuriated. He picked ten Philippine men to serve as runners and trackers. He signaled the Destroyer Cole to land fifteen reserve marines that would give him forty-three marines including the special team. Twenty male Philippine men came forward with their bolos to help. All the bodies were buried. A Philippine male came running out of the jungle and told Sgt. Wells he saw about three hundred insurgents headed south about two miles ahead. Sgt. Wells picked three Philippine men who wanted to be runners and had these men notify Sgt. Kling, Sgt. Zeke, and Pikus. If Pikus and Zeke could close in with him they may be able to kill off many of them and take the pressure off Sgt. Kling's force.

At Cabana Juan, Sgt. Pikus, Wells, and Zeke caught up with the insurgents and annihilated one hundred and fifty of them. Sgt. Pikus' losses included six special team members, five Marines killed, and three wounded. Sgt. Wells' losses were six special team members and four Marines killed with eight wounded. Sgt. Zeke lost five special team members and four Marines killed, seven wounded. Sgt. Pikus dispatched two runners to Sgt. Kling to tell him he believes about one hundred insurgents were headed Kling's way. Kling only had forty-three men so he asked the Army for one hundred and fifty soldiers to set an ambush and finish the job. Two trackers told Kling they saw Emilio Aquinaldo with about twenty-five men headed for Manila. He was wearing an American military campaign hat with a star and dressed in khaki pants and shirt. He had metals on the shirt. They knew him.

The ambush was set just in time. What the Army didn't kill the Philippine runners and trackers with their bolos slaughtered the remaining. Dead or alive, talk about revenge. In the fight Kling and his special team fought their way in and grabbed Aquinaldo the leader. It was May 23, 1901 the Army had a lot of mopping up and the Philippine insurrection ended 1902.

Kling lost eight of his special team capturing Emilio. Captain Smith told Kling to take stock of what was left of the team. The special teams lost twenty-five men, and ten Navy men. The remaining ten Navy men wanted to rejoin their ships. There were twenty-five Marines of the special team left. Colonel Smith said he was going to ship these men with thirty more Marines to the island of Samoa, Pago Pago where we were to be a guard unit and stop the trouble in American Samoa.

Before they shipped out to Samoa Sgt. Pikus and Kling had to go to the Army Hospital in Manila and have grenade and pieces of shell fragmentation dug out of their arms and legs. Sgt. Zeke and Wells had to have stitches in their arms and legs. Five other Marines had to be treated for other wounds. "What Price Glory!"

Chapter 3

It was at this time in history that the jealous Army and Navy higher uppers wanted to disband the Marine Corps. The Army generals and Navy admirals said the Marine Corps was so small, only thirty-five hundred men, that the Army and Navy could do without the Marines. President Roosevelt said the Marines had the only reliable foreign intelligence service he had seen in the last two campaigns. "The Marines stay!" He wanted two thousand more Marines.

While in the hospital Colonel Smith came and said the President of the United States recommended Sgt. Edward Pikus and Sgt. Walter F. Kling for battle commissions as Second lieutenants in the United States Marine Corps. They could keep the special unit intact. Now our special unit had one colonel, two captains, two sergeants, two corporals, and sixteen Pfc.s twenty-five men total. "Away we go."

The president also recommended Colonel Smith to be his Chief Intelligence officer and he would personally notify the Army and Navy Departments to cooperate with Colonel Smith. "Smith may sit in at any military meetings with the Secretaries of Defense." Colonel Smith received a star as Brigadier General. His orders would come directly from the President of the United States, "free lance". He would operate as a free agent. Smith had to remain in Manila with Captains Byrnes and Dell Rico.

They boarded the Destroyer Cole for the trip to Samoa. In all They had fifty-two Marines. General Smith's orders were for our special teams and the additional marines to pack full gear including extra ammunition. Lt. Kling was told to land on Tutuila with twenty-six Marines and Lt. Pikus was to land on the island of Aunu Manu with twenty-six Marines. No trouble was expected. However, there was some trouble makers reported with weapons on both islands. Lietuenants Kling and Pikus were also to report to a Navy Commander names Jones who was in charge of six small islands called American Samoa. A few diplomats from the Secretary of State and Interior were around.

Before Lt. Pikus shipped to Aunu Manu Lt. Kling quartered his men and made sure both sections were well fed. "What a meal!" Roast pig with navy baked beans, sweet yams, fried plantains, baked fish, and native jungle juice. There were two "nookie" houses on the island. "Does it get any better than this?" Our job on the islands was to be security and help establish the government. They were to be the police and fire departments and drive out the old methods and corruption. A couple of dissentious males cut up some of Lt. Kling's Marines while they were out on patrol. Lt. Kling caught them all in a "nookie" house and hung four of them in the village square. A warning- you don't cut up U.S. Marines on duty. Lt. Kling was given the power of judge and punishment.

Meanwhile, Captains Byrnes and Dell Rico with sixty Marines were shipped to the island of Guam. They were to build a Marine barracks. It was now January 1903 and Lt. Kling and Lt. Pikus requested a change of post and unknown to them Captains Byrnes and Dell Rico also requested a change from General Smith. General Smith said that including himself Byrnes, Del Rico, Kling, Pikus as well as Sergeants Brucie Wells and Saprano would on the second of February 1903 at 0900 hours board the USS Merrill at Manila for passage to Marine Barracks San Diego, California. We had to leave the remaining Marines of our groups on Samoa. On board the Merrill only one day at sea Captain Dell Rico started with the Spanish lessons and knife fighting again. They were taught how to do intelligence work all the tricks including how to act, secure information, some psychological testing skills, quick-witted alertness, stress, comprehending situations, obtaining knowledge, and transmitting news. They were also taught how to act out the part we would be playing. They learned Semaphore alphabets and Morse code. Dots and dashes were mandatory. General Smith said with Captain Byrnes' help they would have daily exercise classes. He said we would stop at the Naval shipyard at Pearl Harbor, Hawaii. It would be at least one month before we docked at San Diego. If we behaved ourselves we would be given a three day pass leave in Honolulu so we could get drunk, sit on the beach, sight see, or "nookie' hunting. "O Happy day!"

After three days leave we all returned to the ship for our daily schedule on board ship.

0500 - 0515 reveille
0520 – 0545 exercise
0600 – 0715 breakfast
0725 – 0845 police call
0900 – 1200 drill, jujitsu, knife fighting
1201 – 1300 lunch
1305 – 1700 schooling on intelligence work
1730 – 1830 dinner
1830 – 2200 free time
2200 taps

After being docked at the Naval Base for three weeks the ship set course for San Diego on March 18, 1903.

Before we left Pearl Harbor our mail caught up with us. Ed had three letters from his girlfriend and I had four from mine. Comparing letters they both indicated the girls wanted more of us. We docked in San Diego on March 27, 1903. General Smith said to report to the CO at the Marine Barracks A-2. We were to be quartered there, eat meals with the regulars but were not allowed to communicate with them or anyone else. Our group was headed by General Smith. We soon received orders. General Smith Captain Byrnes and Sgt. Mike Saprano were ordered to Marine Barracks Washington, D.C. Captain Dell Rico was ordered to Marine Barracks San Juan, Puerto Rico. Lieutenants Pikus and Kling Sergeants Zeke and Wells were ordered to stay at Marine Barracks San Diego. Two new Marine recruits Pfc.'s Frank Eckert and Charles Sambach were transferred to our group. Kling and Pikus were to test the two Marines for one week. Psycho, psychics, and Marine indoctrination, if these men were to qualify we were to take them with us to our new post the Marine's Barracks Rifle Range Detachment at Quantico, Virginia. If they did not qualify we were to leave them in San Diego. Train tickets, money, and instructions were all left by General Smith. After two days testing and observing the new Marines the four of us agreed "Four O" and Sgt.s Zeke and Brucie Wells put the men under severe training for our type of work. Kill or be killed!

Since Lt.s Pikus and Kling had special passes they left the new men in the care of Zeke and Wells. Pikus called the hospital where our nurse girlfriends worked. Betty who he talked to was so happy she started to cry over the phone. Betty and Ann were both operating room nurses and their shift ended at three-thirty. Pikus said we would pick them up. Ed and I arrived at the hospital at 1530. Other nurses at the hospital gave us the eye and one said out loud, "What hunks!" Why not? Ed was 5'9 inches tall weighed 175 pounds, blond hair, good looking. I was 5'9 ½ inches 172 pounds blond hair and also good looking. "What does modesty mean?" The girls were still together living in a two bedroom apartment. We had a ball for two nights. Ed and I knew the girls were about thirty-five years old. Both girls proposed marriage. They said they loved us from the start and hoped we both had the same feelings for each of them. Pikus and Kling could not believe what they were hearing. Do things happen like this? Pikus and Kling both looked at each other and said "Why not?" We had nothing else but the Marine Corps in this world. We told the girls we were a bad risk. We may only be able to see them maybe thirty days a year, we did not make much money, and the Marine Corps would have to come first. The girls said they would take us regardless. We again told the girls they would be making a big mistake. They said they would take that chance and then both girls said it would be an asset to the world to have our children. Pikus said first we would have to get General Smith's permission and second we were being transferred to the East Coast. Betty said if you two could find housing for them nearby they would leave their jobs in San Diego. "Operating Room Nurses are in demand. Nurses with eight years O.R. supervision experience should be able to get a job at any hospital." We telegraphed General Smith who gave us his blessing. We were married by the post chaplain the day before we were scheduled to leave San Diego. We told the girls we would look for housing near a hospital and our base. The girls would have to take care of their certification moving and other problems. We would not be able to help. Our problem would be location and housing. Each of our wives said they had sufficient saving and for us to not worry about money. However, we went to the post paymaster who telegraphed General Smith who said that we both had on record three hundred dollars and for him to pay us. The money Ed and I had in savings was used for our uniforms and boots when we were promoted to Second Lieutenants. We gave our wives one hundred fifty dollars each for expenses. We both had a one day honey moon that we spent in bed.

We returned to the base and our Sergeants' reports on the new Marines stated they passed all the requirements. Ed and I reported to the base CO. that our job was completed. We were leaving the base. We departed the next morning. The six of us boarded the train and were on our way to the Marine Barracks Quantico, Virginia it was April 2, 1903. We arrived in Virginia on April 8, 1903 and telephoned our wives at the hospital before reporting to the CO. at the Rifle Range Detachment. Captain H. Walker was in charge of the rifle range. The Captain told us his orders for us were to not shave, cut our hair or mustaches for the week. We were able to clean our bodies and clothes only. We were to familiarize ourselves with and fire the Springfield rifle .30 cal., the Breech-loading magazine bolt type model 1903, practice firing the .45 cal. Revolver, and hand grenade throwing. We were to fire the Springfield from 500 and 300 yards prone position, 100 yards off hand. "Again, do not shave any hair from your bodies." After seven days General Smith came to Quantico and took our group of six men to a restricted area. He told us he had a mission that needed immediate attention. He gave us clean but worn ragged clothes. The kind some males wore in the Caribbean areas. We were going to Panama, two units with three men each. Someone was trying to start up a revolution. We were to fan out all over Panama and get some names of the trouble makers to see if we could find the reason for the unrest. We would be landed at spots above and below the city of Colon on the Caribbean side. A small Navy destroyer would land us at night. Small boats would take us in to shore. They would pick us up at the designated spot between one and four am.

After three days in Panama on the fourth night April 20, 1903 we would be picked up. Since we all spoke and understood Spanish we should be able to get around. We were given contact names and locations for food and information. We could only take our knives, .38 cal. Revolvers, and fifteen rounds of ammunition and one hand grenade. No food. We had to live off the land or rely on our contacts for food and equipment. We had some maps and signals. Lt. Pikus, Sgt. Wells, and Charlie Sambach would be Unit 1 Lt. Kling, Sgt. Zeke, and Frank Eckert Unit 2. Unit 1 was landed above Colon at 2230 on April 20. Unit 2 was landed below the city at 2355. Panama is a small country about 99 square miles. The mosquitoes and bugs were insufferable. We were told by General Smith the reason for this trip had to do with the United States reviving the Monroe Doctrine. The Monroe Doctrine as history related was written when James Monroe was president. It was written by John Quincy Adams. The Monroe Doctrine notified the world that no part of the Americas was to be influenced or opened to European colonization. The United States would protect the weaker countries. Interfering with the independence of countries in the Americas would be considered a serious act of enmity. President Roosevelt wanted to have a canal built across Panama which was at the time a part of Colombia. Columbia refused the right of way to the United States. Panama a part of Columbia declared independence and broke away. The United States recognized Panama's independence. Panama said that if the US would help them they would give the US permission to build the canal to connect the Atlantic and Pacific Oceans. The United States needed a canal for many reasons. It took too long for ships to sail from the Atlantic around South America to the

Pacific Ocean.

Unit 1 was landed five miles north of Colon. Brucie Wells was the lead scout. He had a nose for it. He smelled out a whore house at the first barrio we came to. Wells had more faith in whores than the villagers. One of the girls told Wells that four mean Colombian men who the whores believed were soldiers were living in a small shack about a quarter of a mile up the road. One of the Colombians beat up one of the whores because she refused to perform oral sex on him. The Colombians also beat up villagers and took money and food from them. Unit 1 started up the road headed for the shack. About 100 yards before reaching the place four shots were fired at them. No one was hit. Lt. Pikus fanned out to the left Sambach to the right. Wells ran forward threw his grenade and that was the end of the shack. However, two men came out shooting. Sambach shot both of them. We found some maps, money, guns, and papers that looked like a code was written on them. Unit 1 went back to the barrio to get something to eat and get some sleep.

The next two days Unit 1 visited eight barrios around the jungles. All the people said they wanted independence for Panama from Colombia. The men that were killed at the first barrio were soldiers. Unit 1 had two more skirmishes, one outside Cristobal where three men tried to cut up Unit 1. The three men were shot by Wells and Sambach. Then at Belen in a fire fight Wells killed two men. Sambach had a bullet crease on the right side of his behind and Wells' right ear was nipped by a bullet. Lt. Pikus came down with malaria again.

Unit 2 had a fire fight at Chepo. Three men had found out about them and tried to ambush them. A grenade from Zeke and four shots by Eckert and Lt. Kling ended the party. The three men had maps and papers on them. Unit 2 checked out their areas and found the story the same, independence for Panama. Lt. Kling now had malaria too.

Units 1 and 2 were picked up by the destroyer. All the information from the contacts and both units were sacked and ready to be shipped under guard to General Smith who had them shipped to the hospital at Quantico, Virginia and under quarantine for twelve days. While they were isolated from the rest of the hospital they were given books on espionage, sabotage, and explosions and were told to study. Lieutenants Pikus and Kling were the only two malaria casualties in the units. Sambach's behind was patched up as well as Wells' ear. Before leaving the hospital the enlisted Marines had their clothes surveyed. Lt.s Pikus and Kling scrounged some field clothes. Officers had to buy their own uniforms. They were given a yearly allotment in their pay.

General Smith gave Units 1 and 2 thirty days leave and when the furloughs were over they were to report to the Rifle Range Detachment at Quantico, Virginia for qualification of the 03 Springfield rifle, .45 cal. Revolvers, the new .30 cal. and the Browning water cooled machine gun. Both units would be quartered at the Rifle Range for two weeks.

Lt. Pikus telephoned the hospital in San Diego and caught Betty just as she was leaving Pikus told her we would be looking for houses and would be in touch. Betty said to tell Kling not to worry about money that she had enough to buy a house and then some. She believed Ann's finances were equal. She would tell Ann and Pikus should call her back the next day at 1300 at the hospital. Pikus called back and Betty told him that Ann said to shoot the works. Pikus did not tell the girls they had furloughs. Pikus and Kling found out that new homes were being built on the outskirts of Alexandria, Virginia. They traveled to Alexandria and were very happy at what they found. They each put a deposit on a new house on a 100 x 100 foot lot. Pikus' house was Lot #1 and Kling's was Lot #2. Two bedrooms, one bath, kitchen, dining room, and a large living room with a fireplace, a cellar, steam heat with coal furnace, electric water heater, sewerage, and telephone for four thousand dollars each. They each put two hundred dollars deposit on the homes they selected. The remaining balance would be payable in six months at 3% interest. A new hospital was just completed two blocks from their homes. "The Lord was with us." Pikus telephoned Betty and told her to start the transition. We hoped they could be out in a month. He also told her the cost of the houses and they each mailed a check for eight hundred dollars for furniture, appliances, and landscaping. Our houses were ready to move into before our furloughs ended July 2, 1903. It took Betty and Ann three and a half months before they could travel east.

After the Rifle Range they were ordered back to the training battalion at Quantico for field problem training. The engineering platoon and two Army captains schooled them on land mines, demolition, explosives, and the use of grenades for security. The units remained at the training battalion.

Panama signed a treaty with the United States on November 18, 1903. The next day Kling and Pikus requested a family hardship leave for three days from General Smith and he gave them one week when he found out they were picking up their wives and the new homes were ready for them. Pikus and Kling were to report back to the training battalion at Quantico on November 27 at 1300 hours. The new wives were met at the Washington Station at 100 hours November 21st and taken to their new homes where they were both very happy. They said that after setting up house keeping they would apply to the hospital for positions. They reported back to the training battalion and were happy to be back together with Sgt.s Zeke, Brucie Wells, Corporals Eckert, and Sambach. Captain Dell Rico was ordered back to our units at Quantico and we were all happy to see him. General Smith, now Major General Smith was an Assistant to the Commandant of the Marine Corps at Washington. Promotion time Captains Dell Rico and Byrnes were now Majors, Lieutenants Kling and Pikus were First Lieutenants, and Sergeants Zeke, Saprano, and Brucie Wells were Sgt. Majors, and Corporals Eckert and Sambach were now Buck Sergeants. "The Lord was there again."

Unknown to Units 1 and 2 Major Gen. Smith had interviewed twelve Marines for their units two Marines were telegraph and telephone trained and two were office clerks both of them could speed type and write. There was also a lawyer who was a Second Lt. and he wanted some military experience. He was twenty-five years old and his uncle was a lawyer and a Senator. One Marine had experience on code laws. All the special Marines were in the corps for two years or more with good records. The lawyer was only in the corps for one year. The other six Marines were from a new MP Platoon one had the rank of Corporal, the others were Pfc.s. Major Gen. Smith told major Dell Rico to put the new twelve marines with the help of Units 1 and 2 through hell for two weeks. They must meet our qualifications and those that did not qualify were to be put in the guard company at Quantico.

It was now December 15, 1903 and it is hard to believe all twelve Marines passes all the tests and qualified with their weapons. A new two floor barracks was just completed and it would house sixty Marines. Major Gen. Smith said it was to be our new home. The barracks on each floor had a good size wash room and head. The new steam heat was not yet installed. Each floor had two pot belly coal stoves with a stove to heat hot water. The first floor had an office, guard room, and sleeping quarters for twenty Marines. Lots of room and a few closets. The second floor had a telegraph and telephone room, interrogation office for our lawyer, a code and file room with a large safe. Major Dell Rico had a private office. Officer's quarters, one for Major Dell Rico and for Lt.s Kling, Pikus, and the lawyer with a private washroom and head. Sgt.s Zeke, Wells, Eckert, and Sambach each had a room and one large room for the special Marines. All other Marines were quartered on the first floor. The first floor also had an office and reception room. The ground floor entrance was admissible by special credentials and there was a guard on duty 24 hours a day. There was a back door but no stairs. The door had a security lock. Fire equipment and two fire axes were on each floor all windows were screened. All personnel kept their issued fire arms in one small office on the ground floor that served as the armory. Small arms, rifles, pistols, ammunition, gas and hand grenades were kept there. The

33

sign on the front entrance said Logistics Offices – USMC. The building was actually for USMC Intelligence and Support Intelligence units. All personnel was medically examined, fingerprinted, and received a new dog tag with the letter U1 and their serial number.

On December 19 the Intelligence Units moved into their new home.

The PFC.s had the stoves hot, rooms warm. The day and night guards were responsible for taking care of the pot belly stoves. For heat they had to bring up coal and empty the ashes. Since Christmas was near Major Gen. Smith said for Dell Rico to give the Marines as much leave as he could until January 5, 1904. The building had to be guarded twenty-four hours daily and no unauthorized persons were allowed in at any time. The Marines living and working in the building were not to tell anyone of their duties and that included family. If anyone should ask they were instructed to just say they were doing transportation and supply paper work. No personal telephone calls in or out of the build were allowed.

Major Gen. Smith said he would send nine Marines from a Military Police unit to our small units. Sgts. Zeke's and Wells' job would be to qualify them. We would now have fifteen MP Marines. Sgt. Wells and Sgt. Zeke were in charge of training which included drill, weapons inspections special school, guard duty, police call, building heat, maintenance, and transportation.

Major Dell Rico asked Lt. Kling if he could stop and see his new home over the holidays. He said he was getting married on January 3 (a quiet wedding). He was marrying Major Byrnes' sister whom he had known for years and he would need a house and property. Major Dell Rico stopped with his bride to be and Major Byrnes on Christmas Day and they liked what they saw. Lt, Kling gave Dell Rico the builder's telephone number and he immediately telephoned the builder. As luck would have it the builder was home and Dell Rico told him he would like to buy lots 3 and 4 the same size as Kling and Pikus had. They would get together the next day. We had an enjoyable evening. The street we were on to my knowledge had no name. I think it should have been called Marine Way. Major Gen. Smith said he would like to take our units out for dinner one night to the Port Side with Pikus, Wells, and Eckert and the following night with Kling, Zeke, and Sambach. Major Dell Rico and Byrnes were to make the arrangements with the Marine Inn on Route 9 between January fifth and ninth.

Our T.O. was now

Major General Smith

Major Dell Rico	Lt. Jones	Major Byrnes
Lt. Kling	Lawyer	Lt. Pikus
Sgt. Zeke		Sgt. Wells
Sgt. Eckert		Sgt. Sambach
7 MPs		7 MPs

Brucie Wells, Zeke, Sambach, and Eckert were to train the fourteen MP Marines for our units effective January 11 for two weeks.

January 28, 1904 Major Gen. Smith telephoned Major Dell Rico to have their units squared away for a complete inspection on February 3. After inspection he said Unit 1 with Lt. Kling in command with Sgts. Zeke and Eckert to take their seven MPs to San Juan, Puerto Rico for two months island training. They would leave on February 10 on the Destroyer Dailey out of Norfolk, Virginia at 1400 hours. Lt. Pikus with Sgts. Brucie Wells and Sambach with Unit 2 and seven MPs were also leaving on the Dailey the same day and hour. They were going to Guantanamo Bay, Cuba. They were to stay at the Marine Barracks and receive the same type of training as Unit 1. Major Dell Rico gave Lt. Kling and Lt. Pikus two days leave to see their wives. Both of their wives had found employment at the local hospital which was happy to employ experienced nurses with supervisory experience.

Major Dell Rico would be the liaison Officer for Major Gen. Smith. Major Byrnes would take command of our home base. He would train the remaining Marines, specialist, and our lawyer who we named Spike. Our units training in the

Caribbean areas should be back at home base by May 1, 1904. Other than military courtesy to other officers and Marines our units were on installations and logistics and anyone wanting information would have to contact Major Gen. Smith's office in Washington D.C. Any member of our unit who took the intelligence oath and broke it by giving out confidential information would be severely punished, court martialed for treason, and in some cases the death penalty. Our work was for the safety and security of our citizens and country.

MARINE CORPS

Chapter 4

May 4, 1904. Confidential reports made by our ambassadors, statesmen, and business people to our State Department said that there was a lot of unrest in the Caribbean islands where we had an interest: Haiti, the Dominican Republic, Puerto Rico, Cuba, Panama, and Nicaragua. The State Department gave the reports to Major General Smith who was now known by the inner circle as Head of the Intelligence units for our country. The reports were analyzed by Major General Smith, Majors Dell Rico, Byrnes, Lieutenants Kling and Pikus were also called in. The meeting took place at Major General Smith's office in Washington D.C. Major General Smith told us to get the units in shape to handle this job. Necessary precautions should be taken. If anything goes wrong we would be the goats, that's politics in the State Department. Number 1 find out if there is any intervention of foreign countries, if there is track down their agents and dispose of them. The deep six. Number 2 Look for rebels or insurgents and find out their intentions deliberate or express purpose. If they have demonstrations cause trouble. Deep six the leaders. Watch your actions the State Department boys will be checking. If you have to push a few aside then do it. Try always to keep your identification a secret.

While Unit One was training in Puerto Rico they noticed a change in many locations and past friendships. Inquiring around they were told a Spaniard by the name of El Toro was causing some unrest in the islands. Now they say they are one thousand islands in the Atlantic and Caribbean areas. Many islands of all sizes were passed over that no one claimed since the Spanish American war in 1898. There were no lakes, rivers, or wells on these islands. With no water and not too much vegetation who needed them. There were only native fishermen who caught rainwater.

Lieutenant Kling telegraphed a report to Major General Smith who telegraphed back and said he wanted immediate action. Further investigation by Kling and his command revealed that this Spanish person called El Toro was a trouble maker on every island he could reach and was yellowing out independence for all islands. He was trying to start a revolution on all the inhabited islands. He may be located on one of two waterless islands either Paradise Partido or Parte DeBol.

Lt. Kling could only find two sailboats and one small steamboat without involving the Navy. It was always a lot of reports to fill out when the Navy was involved. We Marines like to improvise. Kling decided to take Sgts. Zeke and Eckert with him to look for El Toro on the Island of Paradise Partido. He would leave the seven MP Marines at the barracks in San Juan. The small steam boat did not look to healthy. The old Puerto Rican who owned the boat said we could make it anywhere. He would be the piloto (sailing master). He had plenty of wood and coal. "Away-we-go sharks and all."

We armed ourselves with .38 cal. revolvers, twenty-five rounds of ammunition, our field packs, canteens, compasses, knives, and one .03 Springfield rifle with twenty-five rounds. We also had six hand grenades. We all looked like bums wearing dirty ragged clothing with long hair and we hadn't shaved for a week. We were playing the paisanaje (peasantry). We would have to live off the land for food. Our piloto said he had fished off the island of Paradis Partido. A small landing dock was about one thousand yards from the town. The town was called Juno. It had one copia Abundancia (store), one barra (bar), and one house of idolat rous desire (whorehouse), and a dozen shacks. The store and bar were owned by Puerto Ricans. The fishermen, farmers, and store owners were a trade for trade business, not much money around. Fresh fish, fruits, and homemade rum would be traded with the store who then traded with the main and nearest island Puerto Rico for cash only. The island was approximately one mile by a half mile in size. Our piloto spoke to the store owner and told him we were after El Toro, the store owner was very happy to get rid of El Toro. He said El Toro would steal from them and rape their women. He told our piloto El Toro had men about twenty-five of them. They had a shack at the turn in the road. El Toro was not on the island. They believed he was on his way to Parte DeBol or to Pinero Island near Cuba.

Kling and his Marines decided to kill or capture a man or two of El Toro's cut throats. Some one notified the rebels because as Kling and his Marines walked down the road shots were fired at them from the shack. Zeke went around to the back of the shack and threw a grenade while Eckert threw a grenade through the front window. The shack unknown to us was loaded with boxes of small caliber ammunition, a 30-40 Krag Manlicher Carcane, and Mauser rifles. Bullets were flying all over. They had to stay down or get hit. A hot one fell on Eckert's hand. No damage. When the lead stopped flying around the area we looked around. The shack was completely demolished. Fourteen men and one woman died. Pieces of shotguns and revolvers and live ammunition was all over the area. One male person they did not notice at first was a survivor. They grabbed him and hung him spread Eagle by the ankles, dropped his pants and started asking questions. He said he did not know anything about the El Toro gang. Since he did not know anything they told him we were going to get him a hot Turkish bath to refresh his memory. He watched as Sgt. Zeke built a fire and put a metal rod in it. Sgt. Eckert put a pair of gloves on and started to oil up the lucky survivor's rectum and private parts. "Boy did he get the message!" He told them everything he knew and then more about the locals. Kling branded him on the left cheek of his behind with the initials MC so he would not forget the Marines. Aren't we lovable bastards? Then they let him go. One of us always has a branding iron in his pack about a foot in length. We use it as a persuader. If a woman gets branded with MC on her behind she could make a fortune.

We had a fish dinner made by the store owners so they stayed over night. Zeke and Eckert checked out the whorehouse. Kling stayed behind. He was a married man.

We returned to San Juan, Puerto Rico. I had Kling's report was telegraphed to the Major General Smith in Washington.

His reply was to carry on. Kling told the piloto to get the boat ready he wanted to check out Parte DeBol Island. The next day Kling had his Marines get their gear together. Same equipment they carried before. Parte DeBol Island was very small, maybe 1000 yards in width by 1500 yards in length. What men were on the island watched as Unit 1 landed then they started shooting. Eckert was shot in the right arm. Zeke was creased by a bullet on his right leg. Sizing up the situation Lt. Kling told his Marines to hit the dirt and stay low. Kling went off to the right with bullets flying all around him. His elbow was creased by a bullet. He was now in a position where he could see the men that were doing the shooting. What fools they were all bunched up. Kling threw his two grenades and knocked out eight men. He then shot the remaining men in their bodies. The bullet wound in Eckert's arm was a flesh wound so they stopped the bleeding and bandaged it. Zeke and Kling's creases were no problem. They stopped the bleeding on the rebel's bodies. They refused to talk. Kling did not waste any time. Zeke started the fire, when the branding iron was hot they dropped their pants and branded each one of them on the left cheek of their behind. They talked so much Kling got tired of listening to them. he destroyed all their weapons and ammunition. Kling told them if he saw them again anywhere he would shoot them. Kling did not find anything else so he left the two rebels with the locals. Zeke located our piloto for the trip back to San Juan.

The report was telegraphed. Major General Smith said to locate Lt. Pikus and check out Pinero Island. "The six of you should be able to handle the problem. Use the MP Marines if you need more men. Good luck!" Kling telegraphed the marine Barracks at Guantanamo Bay. Lt. Pikus was out in the field. Kling left the message for Lt. Pikus to telegraph him at the San Juan barracks in Puerto Rico. Pikus telegraphed back one week later. He said he had checked out Pinero Island with Sgts. Wells and Sambach. The island was a den of the most vicious bunch of killers, thieves, and gang rapers that were causing all the unrest in this area of the Caribbean.

They are well armed with some machine guns, boxes of .30 caliber ammunition, rifles, and revolvers. There are about three hundred of them with twenty whores for service work. Kling made arrangements with the mail and supply Captain to drop his unit off at Guantanamo bay on the ship's way back to Florida. It was now June 15, 1904. Kling, Unit 1, and Pikus with Unit 2 met at Marine Barracks Guantanamo Bay. Pikus telegraphed Major General Smith to tell him about Pinero Island. Major General Smith telegraphed back. "Deep six Pinero Island population. Take one hundred fifty Marines from Guantanamo Bay Barracks if you need help. I want a full report. The C.O. will give you full cooperation also, the Navy for transportation. The Destroyers Johnson and Richey are available. The Destroyers will help if any shelling is required. Free all prisoners and get their reports. Some State Department personnel may be prisoners.

Pinero Island was another waterless island. A few fishermen originally tried to make a living conserving rain water and bringing water to the island in kegs. The island was a half mile in length by one quarter mile in width. The island could be destroyed by shell fire but why do it the easy way. Give the Marines some work. Pinero was northeast of Cuba and well fortified. One report said they had two cannons. Four small towns dotted the island. El Tengo in the north, El Yuno in the south, San Marto in the east, and San Carlos to the west. Lt. Kling would attack from the north. The Navy would land him outside the town of El Tengo. He would push south with Sgts. Zeke, his MP Marines and fifty Guantanamo Marines. From the Guantanamo Barracks each man would have ninety rounds of ammunition, two hand grenades, food, and water for four days. The MP Marines would man the two Browning machine guns. Full field packs. Eight Navy medical corps men, two with each attack unit. Sgt. Brucie Wells with twenty-five marines would land at San Marto in the east to meet Lt. Kling. Sgt. Sambach would be landed in the west at San Carlos Beach and attack to meet with Brucie Wells. All these attack forces would clean up their areas and

41

push south to help Lt. Pikus who was attacking the strongest positions. Fishermen reported that outside the south of El Yuno they counted one hundred and twenty-five well armed men. Lt. Pikus with Sgt. Eckert, his seven MP Marines, and one hundred Marines from Guantanamo would attack the south beach near the town of El Yuno. The seven MP Marines would man the two machine guns. The Navy lobbed in a half dozen shells and tried to smoke the beach. Pikus lost twenty-five Marines in the attack. He set up a defense line with the machine guns and was able to hold. It became a firing match. Back and fourth. Lt. Pikus fell with a bullet in his right leg. Sgt. Eckert took over and moved only about fifty yards forward. Sgt. Eckert was shot in the left arm but kept command. The firing was intensifying by the defenders. These bandits were holding their own. Lt. Kling moved forward after a fire fight losing eight Marines. He was shot in the right shoulder. Sgt. Zeke took command and moved forward meeting up with Sgts. Sambach and Brucie Wells. Both sergeants cleared their areas with minimum casualties. Their attack forces killed about one hundred bandits. The Navy shelled the bandits' position again. All attack units moved forward and the battle was over. El Toro was killed in the battle. Very few prisoners were taken. Lts.Kling and Pikus, Sgt. Eckert and all casualties were moved to the hospital at Guantanamo Bay.

Lietenants Kling and Pikus, Sgt. Eckert after one month at the Bay hospital were moved to the hospital at Quantico, Virginia. Sgts. Zeke, Wells, and Sambach returned to the Logistics Offices USMC for duty. All the Marines from the Logistics Office who participated in the Caribbean clean up were given a month's furlough. Pikus' and Kling's wives were very happy to have their Marines home for awhile. Major General Smith was well pleased. Kling, Pikus, and Eckert were worried that their wounds would force them to take a medical discharge. With the help of god, the doctors, and Major General Smith they would be given the rest of the year to recuperate. Which they did.

They were fit for duty January 6, 1905 and reported to the

Logistics office U.T. Headquarters. Major General Smith said he could not discharge these Marines. They were too valuable to the corps and country.

Chapter 5

Before the month's furlough Kling, Pikus, and Eckert were allowed one month sick leave. Two months off "O Holy Day!" so ended the year 1904.

Reporting back for duty on January 5, 1905 Lt. Pikus received additional duties as Commander of the First and Second Guard companies at Quantico. Lt. Kling was put in charge of the First Training Battalion and Sgt. Brucie Wells was in charge of the Brig and discipline. Eckert and Sambach were to assist him if needed. Zeke and Brucie Wells were promoted to Warrant Officers Third Grade while Eckert and Sambach gained another stripe. There were minor disturbances in the Caribbean areas at this time. It was time that Eckert and Sambach made their bones. Eckert and five Marines were Unit 1, Sambach Unit 2. They both knew their job. After taking care of the minor problems they returned to their former duties. Zeke helped Major Byrnes run the U.T. Units and train the Marines who wanted to join the U.T. Unit Command.

January 10, 1906 Major General Smith called Major Dell Rico, Lt.s Kling and Pikus as well as Zeke and Wells to his office. General Smith said that he had some news that would make them happy. "You five officers are being transferred to San Diego for four months, then to the Philippine Islands for four months to form a new U.T. Unit in the Pacific areas. You will tour Guam, Midway, and the Hawaiian Islands. Sorry but I can only trust you people to get the job done right. You are to check our protectorate and other outlying areas that our country has an interest in. Watch for foreign intervention. Check the people, education, industries, and security. We know we are short on military personnel and equipment. How short? We want the present Philippine Government to start training an Army and Navy. You are to interview and inspect recruits of U.S. Personnel in charge, note the number of Chinese and Japanese moving into the islands. Keep your eyes on the State Department, boys, look for dishonesty and corruption."

In the ten months they found many problems and were shown animosity in all areas. I believe someone put the word out on us. We returned to our home base in the U.S. November 20, 1906. After interrogation and writing out our findings the five of us were given a furlough to start on December 5 ending January 6, 1907. They had to check up on any loose ends in their reports before furlough.

Major Dell Rico, Lt.s Kling and Pikus were greeted home by their wives with much enthusiasm. Their wives said they should invite Major General Smith, his wife, Major Byrnes and friend, also Sgt.s Eckert and Sambach with their lady friends to their Christmas party. The three wives were working on the party before their Marines came home. A good time was had by all and so ended the year 1906.

January 7, 1907 all units and officers returned to the U.T. Headquarters. In March the president said he was going to send a fleet of ships around the world to let other countries know we also had much Naval power. The fleet was known as the Great White Fleet. Sixteen battleships with about fourteen thousand men. It shook the world!

Major Dell Rico was again assigned Liaison Officer to General Smith's office. Major Byrnes was now Commanding Officer of the Second Marine Battalion combat training. Warrant Officer Brucie Wells and Sgt. Sambach would assist him. Warrant Officer Zeke was in charge of the First Marine Cavalry. One hundred mounted Marines. Sgt. Eckert would be his assistant. Always changes.

The Marine Corps needed men. The Navy requested two thousand Marines for ship and base service. The State Department wanted Marines for legation duty. A recruitment campaign was started all over the country. After six months the campaign came up with three thousand recruits. Year 1907 came to a close. It was called The Training Year.

March 2, 1908 Major General Smith relieved Lieutenants Kling and Pikus of their command. The General said we would travel through the Central and South American countries as well as the Caribbean Islands as salesmen. We would represent ourselves as steel pipe replacement engineers, water pipe sales. Our real job was military intelligence. This campaign may take nine months. "Well, they told their wives what to expect by marrying Marines."

"O happy day!" both wives said they were pregnant. Pikus and Kling's wives said there would not be any problems. One wife worked nights and the other worked days. They were nurse supervisors. They could take care of each other's baby. Major Dell Rico's wife and Major Byrnes' intended said they would help when needed. When everything was straightened out Kling and Pikus went to General Smith's office in Washington, D.C. for orders and equipment.

Major General Smith said the slight depression we had in 1907 had helped enlistments. We would have to upgrade requirements. To enlist a male person must be 5'8" tall or over could not be under 5'8" weight 135 lbs. not over 200 lbs. He must read and write English have five fingers, each hand, and five toes each foot. He must pass an eye test reading 20/20. The corps would take male emigrants who lived in the United States for one year and could pass the requirements. They must enlist for seven years to become citizens of the U.S. and receive an honorable discharge.

The reasons for this salesman campaign to Central and South America were five countries in Europe and two in Asia were expanding. They were helping themselves and splitting up the African continent and some islands. Whoever gets their first. The United States needs to know if there is any intervention of foreign powers in the Americas (Western Hemisphere), especially in our protectorates. The five big powers in Europe know we have a navy that will not take any crap from them. They know we have a fair army, but it worries these countries they don't know how many Marines we have. They have heard every Marine is a marksman with a rifle and a terror with a bayonet. They think we have divisions. Some have seen and others heard Marines are tall and not afraid of sacrificing their lives for their country. Teddy did it right!

Lieutenants Pikus and Kling traveled by steamship freight cargo to Santa Cruz, Argentina then to Buenos Aires. They did not find any foreign intervention. What a surprise! They stayed around for two weeks and then traveled to Santiago, Chile where they did not find what they were looking for. Next they went to Bolivia and then Paraguay still nothing. They next hit Brazil, Sao Paolo in Rio de Janiero. Here they found problems. Foreign people from Europe and Asia, agents and spies. Everybody was looking for something. Now Kling and Pikus had the authority to kill (deep six). It took time to seek out and dispose agents that were harmful to the U.S. there were many crazy insurgents that wanted trouble with the U.S. It took underhanded methods to deep six them. After a good clean up Kling and Pikus took off for Caracas, Venezuela. If anyone wants trouble they just have to walk around.

It was night time about 2200 hours and dark when we left our contacts in Caracas. Three males dressed in dark clothes jumped us. Lt. Pikus was stabbed in the right arm. Lt. Kling drew his revolver and shot two of the bandito in the chest. Lt. Pikus' arm was bloody but he managed to grab the bandito who stabbed him by the throat and choked him to death. Lt. Pikus had very large hands. Kling was able to stop the bleeding in Pikus' arm. We had to return to our contacts for medical help in stitching Lt. Pikus' arm. In all the traveling we were unable to contact the Heads of State, Natural Resource people, or anyone interested in American steel pipes. All these countries have enough of their own industrial, internal and private revolutions. What a mess! However, intelligence was our problem. In Argentina we found in many areas the population was made up of Germans, Italians, and Spanish people.

Back to Caracas with the help of our contacts we were able to "deep six" on head of state and two insurgents looking for intervention from a European country. Contacts in all the countries we were in said they would report to our State Department any signs of intervention. We were now on our way to Colombia. What a mess! Our contacts here

47

had control. The banditos were giving Americans trouble. There were assaults, thefts, robbery, and in one case killing of one American woman. We did not find any signs of foreign intervention. Pikus and Kling could not get involved with the police or crime problems. They did help some Americans though. In checking our sales office (intelligence office) our contacts said no problems of intervention were found in Ecuador or Peru. Chile had one problem. "Deep six it."

Pikus' and Kling's next stop Panama. Panama was a viper's nest for foreign agents and banditos. Many foreign countries' agents were lurking around. The U.S. Army and medical units were well represented here but the bandito problem required more trained help. Pikus telegraphed our sales office in Washington, D.C. and requested one hundred and twenty-five Marines to clean up the problems. One problem was the workmen on the canal were being shot at on the job site. Assaults, thefts, and robberies were out of control. Mountain ranges ran the length of the Isthmus affording the banditos many hide outs.

It was now September 2, 1908 Pikus and Kling were six months out of the U.S. Contact in Panama notified Pikus and Kling that their request was granted and help would arrive by October 3, 1908. This canal problem had to be better controlled it was costing the U.S. money, workers were killed, and there were work stoppages. Estimations were about three hundred banditos causing the problems. The U.S. Army Medical teams were trying to control yellow fever and malaria. Major General Smith telegraphed the Army Intelligence office outside of Colon to notify the Army that two U.T. Marines were in the area. Pikus and Kling were told to identify themselves to the Army who said they needed help and would cooperate. A Colonel named Wagner said he had heard that Kling and Pikus were the best U.T. men in the services.

September 4, 1908 three U.S. Army soldiers were fished out of the Atlantic Ocean by the Navy. They had been shot and gutted. These three soldiers were missing for about a week. The Army was furious. Colonel Wagner received a note telling him to keep away from the canal. The banditos did not want a canal dug. The U.S. Government now knew a foreign country was in back of this trouble. Some experts were having thoughts about the Kaiser. Colonel Wagner said it may be unlawful but he ordered his men to shoot all banditos even if they surrendered after interrogation. An eye for and eye! Burn their barrios, kill the women who fight and leave them nothing to eat. Another big campaign was on the way. While waiting for the Marines to land Pikus and Kling gathered all the maps and traced the roads and trails on paper. They noted the disadvantages that would render success, the responsibility, the population in the barrios, the drinking water, the food, and the languages which were Arawakan, Caribe, Spanish, and Castilian as well as the names of the head people in the barrios. They had enough information to help the Senior Officer of the Marines to start the campaign. The Army and the Navy would help in all phases. Kling and Pikus decided to explore the mountain area on the north side of the cut. Here they found a trail and followed it for two miles. They regretted it. They knew better than to leave themselves open. Bullets started flying in all directions. Pikus was creased on the right leg. Kling's rifle stock was shattered. It was a good thing Kling was only holding his rifle with his left hand. The four hand grenades they had Kling and Pikus threw in all directions north, south, east, and west then vamoosed down the trail. They returned to the Army U.T. Quarters. Army units were moving in and training waiting for the Marines to arrive. On October 1 Marine Units came in whale boats from the Cruiser Indianapolis. Colonel John Curtis came ashore to the Army U.T. He had with him two officers and two hundred fifty Marines and Warrant Officer Zeke withy fifty horse Marines. "O Happy Day!" Kling and Pikus were so happy to see Zeke. All the Marines were fed and moved into an Army Barracks for sleeping quarters.

October 8, 1908 Colonel Curtis called a meeting which was attended by Admiral Hoover, Two Star Atlantic Fleet, and Captain More representing Admiral Porter, Two Star, Pacific

Fleet, Colonel Wagner Army, Captain Walker, Lieutenants Kling, Pikus, Diller, and Lucas Marine Corps. The Admiral and Colonels received orders from the War Department Washington, D.C. code name "Hook, Line, and Sinker." Admiral Hoover's ships of the fleet were the Battleships Texas and Pennsylvania, Cruisers Houston, and Atlanta, and five Destroyers the Jones, Reuben, Cooper, Peary, and Truxton. This fleet would patrol the coast of Panama on the Caribbean side for any intervention of ships supplying the Bandito insurgents. Admiral Porter's fleet consisted of the Maryland and North Carolina, Cruisers Astoria and Quincy, and Destroyers Tucker, Hull, Turner, Burie, and Sims to patrol the Pacific side of Panama. Porter's fleet will be on the lookout for ships picking up or supplying the insurgents. Two hundred Marines were on the Battleship Maryland. Colonel Curtis would divide his Marines into four columns as scouts supported by four columns of two hundred Army soldiers for each column. Total Army was eight hundred men. One column will start from Colon and work its way west across the Gatun Lake and deep six Bandito insurgents, and burn their barrios. Column two will support Column one and spread out across the Panama Canal zone to La Chorrera then to Cameron. This will not be easy for the men. They will have to deal with the jungle, rain, mountainous country, mosquitoes, and insects. Columns three and four will start at Cativa go to New Limon then to Santa Rosa and up to Madden Dam and the lake areas. They will move on to Chilibre, Pedro Miguel and then to the La Palma area. The areas and towns mentioned are suspected Bandito insurgents hideouts. Other Army units will patrol the building sights. Small Navy boats will patrol Gutan Lake and waterways. This campaign may take two months. It serves three purposes: first for the U.S. to move out and destroy all Bandito insurgents stopping the work on the canal, two it lets the world know no intervention on the Central American countries and three maneuvers Navy, Army, Marines a good work our for the services.

Lieutenants Kling and Pikus received orders to carry

out their U.T. travels. They were to check out Costa Rica, Nicaragua, Honduras, and Guatemala. Kling and Pikus knew they could not finish their U.T. work before February 1909. There were no problems in Costa Rica. Christmas time in Nicaragua contacts told Kling he was the father of a seven pound baby boy. Pikus was the father of a six and three quarters pound baby girl. Both wives were in good health. The contacts would get word back to their wives that they are well and happy. Outside of Managua, Nicaragua Kling and Pikus were shot at while on horseback traveling to Cabezas. There were no signs of foreign intervention. The country had many Banditos who would cut your throat as soon as look at you. Kling and Pikus said they would not recommend Nicaragua for any Americans to vacation at this time. They had to fight their way out of Ocotal a town near the Honduras border Guatemalan contacts said their countries were clear of any intervention but Pikus and Kling checked it out anyway. They boarded a boat out of Belize, Honduras (a banana boat) going to Havana, Cuba and then to Miami, Florida. A train ride from Miami took a day and a half to reach Quantico, Virginia. Pikus and Kling first called their wives before reporting to the U.T. Headquarters. One week of interrogation and written reports. A lot of information could not be written. Pikus and Kling said they were unhappy they missed the Canal Campaign. They were out of the country eleven months. Three weeks leave was granted.

Chapter 6

On March 3 Kling and Pikus reported for duty at the U.T. headquarters Quantico,Virginia. Zeke returned from the Canal Zone and told them the campaign was a big success. The Bandito insurgents lost six hundred men, ten young boys, and twenty women. The Marines lost twenty-five dead and sixty were wounded. The Army had forty dead and sixty wounded. The Navy had three killed and six wounded. German and French weapons and ammunition were found all over the country.

On March 5, 1909 Major General Smith was named Commandant of the U.S. Marine Corps. "The Lord is still with us." Three Star General Alexander retired. Major Dell Rico was now Colonel Dell Rico, General Smith's Liaison Officer. Major Byrnes now Colonel Byrnes, Pikus and Kling were now Captains. Zeke and Wells were Warrant Officers First Grade. Eckert and Sambach were now Battlefield Second Lieutenants. Captains Kling and Pikus, Lt.s Sambach and Eckert, Warrant Officers Zeke and Wells were all relieved of their present duties. They were to report to the Army School at Fort Bliss for six weeks. Three weeks were for State Department and Diplomatic training, two weeks War College, and one week Charm School. Fort Bliss was eight miles outside of Washington, D.C. on U.S. 1 Virginia.

Colonel Dell Rico's wife gave him twin boys weighing six and a half pounds each. He purchased a Model T Ford for nine hundred dollars. Kling and Pikus purchased only one Model T. They all had wheels now and could see their wives more often.

The Marine Corps was expanding it now had twelve thousand enlisted men and one thousand officers. New headquarters were built at Quantico for Intelligence Resources and Special Operations. Our new name was I.R.S.O. Kling, Pikus, Eckert, Sambach, Wells, and Zeke moved in on April 6, 1909. They all had their own rooms on the second floor. They messed at the Officer's Mess in Quantico. The large basement had a Record Room, an Armory, and small arms range, Communication Offices, an Interrogation Room, and a Map and Tracing Room. Guard quarters, Detention, and a Reception Room were all on the first floor. There was twenty-four hour seven day guard. A Sergeant and Pfc. runner armed at the pass door front entrance. Rear entrance emergency only, fire door lock with alarm and lights.

Commandant Smith selected Colonel Byrnes to command I.R.S.O. A general meeting will be called when Colonel Byrnes has everyone settled in. Kling, Pikus, Zeke, Wells, Eckert, and Sambach were the ramrods of I.R.S.O - all field men.

April 6, 1909 Commandant Smith telephoned Colonel Byrnes at I.R. S.O. headquarters in Quantico he said to set up a meeting at HQ. 1000 hours on April 8. "The following named officers are to be present: Captains Kling and Pikus, Warrant Officers Zeke and Wells, Lieutenants Eckert, Sambach, and yourself. Colonel Dell Rico will drive me down. After the meeting a luncheon at the Officers Mess. Inform General Barra. He is the new Base Commander." Four Star General Smith our new corps Commandant and friend for almost ten years was very happy we were all well and healthy. He said he had many good officers but he believed the eight of us were the cream of the crop. Four things the Commandant hated were politics, atheism, disloyalty, and cowardice. With the increase in enlistments. "Watch for them! As the new Commandant I need a true survey of all our possessions and protectorates. Now, let's take the Pacific! How many Marines should be on the following named islands for security and military reasons? Hawaii, Johnston Palmyra, American Samoa, Guam, Midway, and the Philippines. How much artillery is needed? I am sending Lts. Eckert and Sambach as Team 1. Captain J. Amos and Lt. Conway as Team II, and Colonel Jissler and Major Nicholson as Team III. The teams shall leave ten days apart from each other. No teams shall compare information. Each team shall operate separately. The only time they may get together is if a team is in trouble. They shall carry side arms, writing material, compass, rulers, and tape measures, drawing materials, chalk, adding and dividing charts, and full uniforms. Transportation has been arranged with the railroads. The Navy will take care of them when they sign in at Naval Headquarters. Admiral Greens has an office in San Diego, California. Four months are allowed for this survey. The government wants this information like the day after tomorrow. Hallelujah! Captains Pikus and Kling will finish the intervention investigation in the South Atlantic and Caribbean areas. They will also take a military survey and return in three weeks. Warrant Officers Zeke and Wells will assist Lt. Colonel Byrnes on the I.R.O.S. transition."

Kling and Pikus returned three weeks to the date and drove their Model "T" Ford to Washington, D.C. to report to the Commandant. Colonel Dell Rico met them there. After interrogation and checking the reports at the Commandant's Office the Commandant said luncheon was ordered for the four of them at the Rodger Smith Hotel, his brother's hotel. After lunch the Commandant said we would return to his office for new assignments for Captains Kling and Pikus. He gave them three days leave to see their wives then report to I.R.O.S. for equipment.

The assignments were to get into two countries and find out who is causing trouble. Haiti and the Dominican Republic. "Check you Spanish dialects. You are going in as native sons. Get your rags together. Let your hair and mustaches grow. Look like you lived in the regions. Take only your knives and revolvers, twenty-five rounds, and one grenade. Don't kid yourselves this is a very dangerous assignment. You will have contacts in both countries. You are on your own to get in and out of these countries. Use fishermen boats. The Navy will drop you off at Port de Pais, Haiti. About a mile off shore by Marker 1 a fishing boat should be waiting."

On June 15, 1909 they departed from Norfolk, Va. on the Destroyer Richey. They picked up the fishing boat and made the Port de Pais shore at midnight on June 23, 1909. Pikus and Kling met their contact at a pre-arranged shore marker. They were taken to the contact's home. Maps, information, and special instructions were given to Pikus and Kling. They are to sleep out in the open or find shelter in one of the barrios. Eat what they can steal or buy at an outside market. They survived and lived in the field before. One of the pescador (fishermen) said there is a barra (bar) outside of Cap Haitien where many militar (military) and persona (people) met. He said everyone has their hands out. Lots of malo (bad) hombres (men) with "pistols-pistolerus" (pistols). Our first contact told us to be careful about this barra. Watch out who you talk to since you people know the language, "just listen". Our contact because of his position could not get out the information. That's why we had to come in.

After traveling by farmer's carts and walking we found the barra in Cap Haitien. Outside the barra were about fifty saddle horses. About three hundred people were in the area in and out of the bar mostly men, the women were standing around. Pikus and Kling pressed their way into the barra. A tall male was on a keg speaking in Haitien Spanish. He was talking to the people about joining the Revolution. Many advantages, more food, more money. He said his name was Commandante (Captain) Juan Ecpinal. He said all the politicians were helping. Many of the people who had power and money spoke French. They believed Ecpinal was an illiterate Army Private looking to make his mark. The Haitian who wanted a revolution was named Chara Balcze Garza, he was the big shot. His cut throats were illiterate guerillas who loved to cut up blancs and foreigners. The Revolutionists were setting up camps all over the country.

Pikus and Kling traveled to other areas, Port au Prince and Jacmelo. The situations were the same. In Jacmelo Pikus noticed six horses outside of what looked like a barn. He went into the barn while Kling stayed outside. Pikus came out of the barn with his arm bleeding. He said, "The bastard tried to kill me with a machete." Pikus said while trying to purchase two horses and saddles the transaction changed when the bastard saw "I put my hand inside my shirt to get the money from my money belt. I shot him." Kling heard the shot. He stopped the bleeding and used his bandanna. Pikus was lucky it was only a scratch. Pikus and Kling ran toward the beach. No pursuers. They found a fisherman who said he would take them to Barahana, Dominican Republic, Santo Domingo for a price. They boarded his boat and he gave them some cooked fish. He set the sail. The boat also had an old motor. He had an old first aid kit he stole somewhere. They purchased the kit, Pikus needed a clean bandage. He also had a clean shirt that almost fit Pikus.

The fisherman let Kling and Pikus off the boat at a small dock in Barahana. They walked up the path and someone said, "Parada!" (Stop). "Ahdonday vah?" (Where are you going?) Do donde viene?" (Where do you come from?) Behind a big bush two males came out and walked up to them. Pikus winked at Kling. Both of these males were on the ground and died from knife cuts before you could say "doy au los buenos dias." (I wish you good morning.)

Pikus remembered his brother a Marine and cut up in the Philippines,. Anyway they could not be interrogated.

Searching the two males they found by the credentials they carried they were Immigration Police. They had badges and some money. Looking up the hill behind the bushes was a small shack, two mounted horses, saddles with rifles. Kling and Pikus undressed the two males. With some rope and the horses help they dragged the bodies down to the water and threw them in. Like swimming "bare ass"!

You may call us murderers. We have a job to do. If those Immigration Officers took us in we would be tortured. They would inflict severe pain. It would take us days to die.

Pikus and Kling found some clean clothes and uniform shirts. They bathed in the ocean then threw fresh water over their bodies. They heated up some beans and chicken they found in the shack's storage area. They burned the shack, mounted the horses, and rode up the road headed east toward Ciudad Trojillo. They stayed clear of any places or persons that appeared like law enforcement. They stopped at a barrio bar. The seven day week menu was beans and goat meat. The beer was awful.

The people in this area were poor peasants with disease problems. They just went along with their everyday problems, clean drinking water and food. The educated people had money. They ran everything. Pikus and Kling did not locate any insurgents or Revolutionists. There were some guerilla fighters. The local police and government agents were controlling them. Pikus and Kling still had all of their equipment. The horses we had were in good shape. Traveling to San Pedro conditions did not improve. At Santiago conditions changed. As they turned into the main street they were challenged by three males on horseback. Kling went forward to talk to them. One of the males on horseback took his rifle out and shot at Kling. He missed. Pikus had his revolver out which spoke twice. Two dead men. The third man put his hands up in the air. These three males were half police and half bandits trying to make a buck regardless of which you were. Pikus said, "The hell with this." So he shot the third male in the head. No one seemed to be around. They moved the bodies off the road, took what was in their pockets, slapped the horses on the ass, and they took off up the main road. "Some Fun!"

Santiago had all kinds of problems. Revolutionists yelling, "Down with Americano." People running around with guns and machetes. "Boy what a mad house!" Down with the government. Pikus and Kling were told a fellow by the name of Juan Casto Bapisterie was a leader for independence.

Kling and Pikus had enough information. They rode to Port de Pais where they hired a fisherman with a large barco (boat) to take them to Guantanamo Bay, Cuba. It was September 4, 1909. They had to wait for a Navy boat to take them to Norfolk, Va. They arrived in Norfolk September 30, 1909. Their orders were to go directly to Washington, D.C. the Marine Commandants Office and report to Colonel Dell Rico.

After one week of interrogations and written reports Kling and Pikus were granted a three day leave to see their families.

They were then to report to I.R.O.S. Headquarters at Quantico,
Va. October 15, 1909 at 1200 hours.

COLONEL DELL RICO

USS Richey

59

Chapter 7

On October 21, 1909 all hands were notified to check their equipment for wear and tear. Survey the old equipment for new, especially weapons. A meeting will be held for all hands for assignments on October 25 at 0900 hours at I.R.O.S. 1. - Colonel Dell Rico to remain liaison to the Commandant. 2. - Colonel Byrnes I.R.O.S, Commander and 3. - Captains Kling and Pikus new assignments. Warrant Officers Brucie Wells and Zeke to assist on investigating insurgents attacking American citizens, also corruption, lawless marauders in Nicaragua. Nicaragua is a protectorate. Lieutenants Eckert and Sambach to remain at I.R.O.S. headquarters and train new recruits. Kling and Pikus, Wells, and Zeke to board the train at Quantico for Norfolk, Va.on October 30, 1909. At Norfolk the Destroyer Richey is waiting for them. They will board and sail.

A fishing boat named Swan will meet them three miles off the coast near Puerto Cabezas, Nicaragua. It was November 14, 1909. The fishing boat Captain said before dropping them off he may be back to pick them up at the dock at Puerto Cabezas in December. They will receive orders about departing.

Captain Pikus and Warrant Officer Wells left the dock and walked off for San Juan, DeNort. Kling and Zeke were left off at Quilali El Chipote. Pikus and Wells bought two horses and broken saddles at an open market. Since they spoke the language and looked the part they had no trouble. About three miles outside of San Juan, DeNorte they ran into trouble. They were shot at from ambush. They were not hit. They dropped to the ground and returned fire. Pikus went off to the left flank and Wells to the right. Wells spotted four males grouped together firing at our first position. Wells threw a hand grenade and they all bought the farm. Pikus and Wells dragged the bodies to an open pit, searched them, took all their money and weapons, and threw them in. Good meals for the wild life.

At a barrio near Quilali El Chipote Kling and Zeke tired

of walking decided to purchase horses. After the purchase of the horses and other equipment they noticed four males with machetes take off in the same direction they were going to travel. They both checked their revolvers. "Sure as hell is supposed to have fire." About two miles from the barrio the four males came at them swinging their machetes. Kling shot three and Zeke shot one before one could say "Peter caught his finger in a pickle barrel". Zeke said, "What the hell kind of country is this?" They left the bodies on the road and took off. Pikus and Wells rode off to Nicaragua and around Granada Rivas. A lot of bad looking hombres were around but no trouble. They traveled up to Leon liked the location so they stayed a couple of days at a contact's home. Plenty of information, rum, and girls. Kling and Zeke rode up to Blue Fields, a small fishing barrio on the coast on the Caribbean side. The people were friendly, the shelter livable, and the cooked fish delicious. There was only one drawback. Three bad hombres were stealing and raping the people. Zeke spotted a bar and said, "Let's have a drink." While drinking at the bar three men ranging in age about twenty-five to fifty said in Spanish, "Let's knock these two hombres off. They look like they may have some money." Kling kicked one in the knee cap and knifed the other one in the chest. Zeke grabbed the one remaining and knifed him in the belly cutting upward. Kling choked the one he kicked in the knee cap. "Deep six!" They left Blue Fields heroes. The horses were in good shape. They rode to Prinza Polca where they met their first contacts. The contacts treated them like kings. Food, rum, girls, and a fishing trip. "Amen!"

Leaving Leon, Pikus and Wells traveled by horse to Ocotal then to Matagalpa where they met up with a band of insurgents. They had to join up or die. So they faked out as bad guys until they could get away.

Now getting away was not easy. One leader by the name of El Craneo kept his eyes on them. He was a mean looking bastard. This El Craneo had been torturing a male and female tied to a tree. He was using an iron rod that was heated on

61

their private parts. He loved to hear them scream. Pikus said, "I am going to nail that son of a bitch." It was getting dark. Pikus was watching what El Craneo was doing. El Craneo started walking toward an out house. Pikus went around him and waited. No one was around. Pikus was in front of El Craneo when he stabbed him in the stomach then cut his throat. When El Craneo was found everyone was running around looking for the murderer. The insurgents' second leader said it was the opposition that caused the murder. This second leader called El Cuchillero was a beau dressed like a four star General with medals, badges, and bandoleers. Pikus said we were going to "Deep six this guy before we leave." Pikus and Wells waited in the dark outside El Cuchillero's private out house. They grabbed him, slugged him with their revolvers, and then cut his throat. They put his head in the hole of the one seater. Now that the two leaders were gone they decided it was time to vamoose. They still had the horses. Wells said we better check our contacts in Managua.

The trip was long. They were dirty and hungry. There was nothing but poor peasants walking around. The directions they had to the contact's house were not good. They did get to the house but it had been burned down. They were told by the people walking around that men came, shot the owner and family, and burned the house. They toured Managua. Conditions were all the same. Insurgents, revolution talk, how they hated Americano, poverty, this country at this time needed stabilization, money, and leaders that were not corruptible.

Pikus and Wells headed for Blue Fields to find a fishing boat to take them to Cuba. They found a fisherman who had a boat. He said he would take them to Cuba for a price. "All the money up front." They told him they would give him half before and the rest when they reached Cuba. He said to wait at the dock. He had to get fuel. They waited all night, he never came back. Two men in uniforms were looking around the dock. They hid until the uniformed men left. After looking around they saw a capable looking boat. The Captain said he would take them to Havana, Cuba. He was going there for cargo. The boat was a freighter. Before leaving Pikus looked up the dock and saw the boat of the guy that stiffed them. They were not leaving before dark. Pikus and Wells crept up to the boat. No one was around. They set up two hand grenades one across from each door of the cabin. They went back to the rented boat. They were about five hundred yards out in the ocean when they heard an explosion. Wells said to Pikus, "I guess we were justified." Wells and Pikus met Kling and Zeke at the American Consul in Havana. They had an adventurous experience.

It was December 15, 1909 when they all reported to I.R.O.S. headquarters in Quantico, Va. After their reports were completed Pikus, Kling, Wells, and Zeke received a fifteen day leave. They were told to report to I.R.O.S headquarters on January 5, 1910 at 1300 hours. Two days before reporting they were scheduled for medical exams.

Their wives were very happy to have them home over the holidays. The latest news was Colonel Dell Rico's wife had a seven pound baby boy and Colonel Byrnes' bride was pregnant. Betty and Ann said they would like to have another child. They both looked at their husbands and said we will talk about this later. Pikus looked at Kling and said, "Why not, the Marines need more men." Parties, visiting each others homes, and shoveling snow was great. Zeke, Wells, Eckert, and Sambach stayed half of the time between Kling's and Pikus' houses. All their children were healthy. Pikus' and Kling's wives were doing well at their jobs at the hospital. Both wives had managed to save money. "Thank the Lord!"

WE WERE MARINES

KLING

PIKUS

ZEKE

WELLS

SANBACH

ELKERT

Chapter 8

After receiving medical clearance Pikus and Kling reported to I.R.O.S. headquarters on January 5, 1910. They surveyed and turned in equipment. Eckert, Sambach, Wells, and Zeke were already in the meeting room. Colonel Dell Rico walked in he said, "At Ease!" Then he greeted them. He said your next assignments are internal, American Native Indian Tribes. He asked for volunteers, he received six. He said the problem was this: the appropriation for Indian affairs has doubled in the past year with the decrease of the American Indian Tribes and population something was wrong. The Indians from many tribes wrote in about conditions. President Taft asked Commandant Smith if he could help. He said he has seen and heard of the I.R.O.S' work. He needed people he could trust. Commandant Smith said he would help, but he needed a free hand for his men. Their decisions and the license to kill. Commandant Smith received authorization, free hands, and equipment. Commandant Smith and Colonel Dell Rico set up the procedure.

Clothes – all agents to dress the same. Western style – dungarees or corduroy trousers, depending on climate conditions. Two inch black trouser belts. Two (2) pair trousers each, four (4) pockets.

Shirts, one woolen and one light weight both light blue.

One light weight and one heavy weight Western style jacket.

Two (2) blue bandanas each.

One (1) pair riding boots and one (1) pair dress boots – Western style.

All agents to wear cowboy large style blue hats.

1- each short Mackinaw plaid coat.

1- each heavy woolen blanket.

1- each rubber or oiled cloth poncho

1- 2 quart canteen

1- 25 foot lariat

1- pair hand cuffs – two keys

1- (8) eight inch Bowie knife

1- pen knife – 3 inch

1- saddle bag – 2 sides- leather

2- hand grenades

2- smoke grenades

1- saddle – complete

1- horse blanket – horse feed bag – 1 horse brush – bridle

1- cartridge belt – 30 rounds with leather holster – hip style.

1- short 45 cal. Revolver, single or double action – sixty rounds of ammo

1- leather rifle case on horse

1- Winchester rifle carbine model 94 – 30-30

3- boxes of 30 x 30 ammo

Writing paper – pencils – pen statement blanks

2- badges – one US Marshal

1- USIF – Indian Agent Card type credential with left and right fingerprint – Indian Agent age, eyes, height, Dept. Serial Number. Names of Indian Agents, license, location of reservation. Inventory stock and beef on hand (food). Monthly allotment for each Indian, surplus and disposition, clothing, blankets, also sanitary items disbursement.

Indian agents found corrupt, falsifying records or record books already falsified shall be arrested and turned over to a U.S. Marshall who will place them in the nearest U.S. detention center or county jail. No bail shall release the corrupt person. The Dept. Of Indian Affairs Washington, D.C. upon being notified shall send a replacement. Indians aware of what was going on but were afraid to speak may now sign a Statement of Facts and Treatment. The Indian agents investigating shall count the number of Indians receiving U.S. allotments. Indians shall be fingerprinted and receive a metal tag with their number on it, also the date. The Indians shall also be investigated for corruption and scare tactics among themselves. Indians who have been convicted of crimes by the tribal council and agents shall be turned over to the nearest U.S. Marshall for detention. Investigating Indian agents shall receive five hundred dollars a record of their expenditures. When money is needed they shall notify Indian Affairs by telegraph. Their salaries shall be held in abeyance until they complete their missions. Loss of limbs, death by any other means but suicide shall be compensated for.

Investigating agents on this program Captain Kling and Warrant Officer Zeke were given eight (8) Indian Reservations in Washington State (Ozette, Makah, Quileute, Quinault, Yakama, Colville, Spokane, and Port Madison). It took three months to check them out. While some records were problems one has to realize transportation, sickness, and deaths have reduced the population. These tribes did not ask for more allotments or receive any. The Indian agents were very helpful. Some one back in Washington was cooking the books. Captain Pikus and Warrant Officer Wells checked out seven Indian Reservations also in Washington State ((Puyallup, Muckleshoot, Squaxin, Nisqually, and Skokomish). It took them three and a half months. The agents were happy that some one back in Washington thought about them. They did not receive any additional money, food, or clothing. These Indians in the Northwest could use more money it was unbelievable the way these Indians survived. The white man should stop looking for gold on Indian land and stop poaching on the game and fishing.

Captain Kling's and Warrant Officer Zeke's next assignment was Indian Reservations in Idaho and Montana (Coeur D'Alene, Nez Perce, Blackfoot, and American Falls). Records and allotments checked out. The Indians on the reservations had the same problems with white men poaching on the game and fishing and no increase in money or allotments. In Montana they checked out Blackfoot, Fort Belknap. Fort Peck, Flat Head, Northern Cheyenne, and Crow Reservations. The Blackfoot Reservation books were not in order. They gave the agent whose name was Dillion a week to get them in order or out he goes. In checking back later everything checked out. The Crow Reservation Indians gave them trouble. The Indians and one in particular named "Low Eyes" attacked the agent in charge and put him in the Indian Health clinic with a broken arm and leg. The Indian then took all the food and clothing from the agency. Kling and Zeke called in the Army from Fort Peck. The Army troops arrested "Low Eyes" and took him back to the fort in chains. They then set up a temporary agent and moved in supplies to the agency. The agent in the hospital had been cooking the books. When he gets out of the hospital he will find a U.S. Marshall waiting for him. He will recoup in jail. The other reservations checked out but not to receive a four-o-class. They were told to straighten out. The agents were not happy. Kling and Zeke said if the Indian Police Forces on the reservations they checked received more training and more of a salary it would give the job some prestige and would help to keep the agents honest.

Pikus and Wells checked out Umatilla, Warm Springs, Yakama, and Fort Mcdermit Indian Reservations in Oregon. They all said they had problems. They needed more money. They gave Pikus and Wells the information desired. Pikus and Wells headed for the Hoopa, Round Valley, and the Bid Well Indian Reservations in Northern California. The books and count all checked out. The agents said they needed more money. In Southern California Pikus and Wells took two days vacation. They then headed for Tule, Cahuilla, Santa Rosa, Los Coyotes, Martone, Auga, Gauliente, and Quechas Reservations. The books, count, and conditions were satisfactory. So who is getting the large appropriations? The Indian Reservations say they have not asked for more money but would like more.

Taking trains, wagons, and horseback day in and day out takes a lot out of a man. Pikus and Wells had been out now seven months. The next stop was Reno, Nevada where they said they would take a three day vacation.

Frank Eckert and Charles Sambach now Second Lieutenants were assigned to investigate Foruscororo and Goonandado Indian Reservations in New York State The

Goonandados had no Indian agent. The Tribal Indian Chief said he left two days ago so he was put in charge. The agent said he had to shop for lumber. The warehouse was almost empty of supplies. In checking what records they could find this reservation had asked for and received a check for twenty-five thousand dollars for new buildings and a bridge. The agent had received and cashed the check stating he needed cash to lower the cost of the buildings. Before the agent left he sold almost all of the supplies. A U.S. Marshall was called in. Washington was sending a new agent. Wanted flyers were sent to all Law Enforcements Agencies within fifty miles.

The next stop for Eckert and Sambach was for Foruscororo Reservation. It was a mess! Old buildings were falling down, the water was bad, and the whole area smelled of dirt, tears, and garbage. Washington reports indicated this reservation was receiving three times the allotment. The warehouse was empty of supplies. The Indians said they were living on half rations for a month. Government allotment checks had been cashed. The Indian reservation bank account showed a balance of two dollars. The agent whose name was Miles was pocketing fifteen hundred dollars a month. Eckert and Sambach caught him in time. He was going to take off. A U.S. Marshall placed Miles in the county jail.

The Tribal Chief was named agent until Washington could send one. Food and clothing were brought in by U.S. Army troops. It now appeared employees working in the War Department on Indian Reservations Finance and Administration were working with the Indian agents on large allotments and then receiving a kick back (money). Eckert and Sambach telephoned Colonel Dell Rico requesting a meeting as soon as possible at Army Headquarters in New York City.

Chapter 9

Captain Pikus and Warrant Officer Wells were assigned to check out Turtle Mountain, Devil Lake, and Sioux Indian Reservation in North Dakota, also Yankton and Rose Bud Reservations in South Dakota. They were to report back to I.R.O.S. Headquarters no later than December 10 at 1300 hours. Captain Kling and Zeke were assigned to check out Pine Ridge, Standing Rock, Cheyenne River, and Upper and Lower Brule Indian Reservations in South Dakota. They were also told to report back to I.R.O.S. Headquarters no later than December 10 at 1300 hours. Lieutenants Eckert and Sambach were to report back to Headquarters immediately for Washington, D.C. Investigations. Pikus and Wells had no problems with Turtle Mountain and Fort Berthold Reservations. Clean bill on both Indian agents. The Devil Lake Sioux had troubles; fights, thefts, killings, and stealing government food, clothes, guns, and ammo. The Indian Police were not trained to handle these problems. Pikus called Fort Totten and after he gave the correct code he requested two hundred soldiers to surround the reservation. The 10th Cavalry had a company of black troopers who were top fighters in the area and two old Indian fighter friends U.S. Marshall Jess Walker and Sheriff Billie Graham. Pikus did not know it at the time but Jess and Billie were after the Indian who started the trouble at Devil Lake Sioux. The Indian had caused trouble in their jurisdiction. This Indian trouble maker had caused two deaths at Devil Lake. He had about thirty-five followers. His name was Black Cloud. The Indian agent said he was a bad Indian. He had trouble with him when he was younger. He was on and off the reservation for ten years, always in trouble stealing. Captain Rufus James and his two hundred troopers caught thirty of the trouble makers. James had them tied to a post and then his men took turns applying the whip. Ten lashes each. Then he branded each one with a small "T" on their right leg. Two Indians were killed. They were the group involved. James had the power to hang all of them. He gave them a warning

70

of what would happen if he found any of them in trouble again.

Pikus, Wells, U.S. Marshall Walker, and Sheriff Graham had to leave the reservation to rundown Black Cloud and his followers. The sheriff and Marshall shot four of them in the Rocky area outside the reservation. The Indians were trying to ambush them. Black Cloud shot at Pikus and Wells – he missed. Pikus and Wells didn't.

The Army helped the Agents to get control of the reservation. The next stop for Pikus and Wells was Yakton Reservation in South Dakota. Everything checked out so they went to their last stop Rose Bud Reservation in South Dakota. The Indian agent was having trouble with two young Indians. Pikus and Wells took the two Indians off the reservation for one day, and then brought them back. They were taught to be good Indians.

Pikus and Wells stayed at Rose bud Reservation for one week. They had a lot of reports to write. It was November 15th when they boarded a train for New York City. Pikus said he would like to stop home in Alexandria to see his pregnant wife before reporting in at I.R.O.S. Headquarters. Wells could sleep at his place and they both could drive down to I.R.O.S. together before the 10th of December.

Captain Kling and Warrant Officer Zeke's first stop was Pine Ridge. The Indian agent said his allotments were the same. No change. He was having trouble with six young Indians. They were stealing, drinking, and annoying anyone they could. He pointed out the six. They were walking down the road. Kling and Zeke were on horseback. With their lariats they each lassoed one young Indian and dragged him down the road about fifty yards. The four other young Indians were terrorized. They just stopped walking. Kling and Zeke left the two lassoed Indians on the ground and with their other lariats they quickly lassoed the four young Indians standing together. What a catch! They rode around and wrapped the four Indians and dragged them about fifty feet. They then told the six Indians to get in a line. Kling told them he could give each of them twenty-five lashes or brand them for their misconduct. If they break up their group, behave, get some work, and stop drinking he would let them go. Kling said if he heard any one of them causing problems on or off the reservation he would come back and hang him. The six young Indians were glad to disband and get away from Kling and Zeke. The next stop was Stand Rock Cheyenne Reservation.

The agent said he was getting double the allotments but was not giving any kickbacks. One well dressed fellow came to the agency with the deal. The agent said he grabbed the fellow and threw him out the door of the agency. Everything else checked out. Kling and Zeke went to the Upper Brule Reservation. The Indian agent also said he was receiving a double allotment. No one came around looking for a money kickback. Records and conduct checked out. Their last stop was the Lower Brule Reservation where there were some problems. Kling and Zeke were walking up to the agency building when two well dressed white males passed them. They met the Indian agent at the door and he said, "Those two fellows who passed you asked me for three thousand dollars. They said the government over paid the reservation and they would meet me at the Fort Thompson Bank where the reservation had their account. I was to give them cash". The agent said they had badges and showed him government type credentials. They looked threatening. Kling and Zeke did not stop to identify themselves to the Indian agent. They ran back to their horses and rode after the two well dressed men. They lassoed the two men who started to put up a fight. Zeke cold cocked the big one and Kling wrapped his rope around the other. After putting on hand cuffs and a rope around them they took them back to the agency. The Indian agent identified them. Zeke started a small fire and took out his small branding iron with the letter "M" on it. One of the thieves said, "What are you doing?" Zeke said, "We are going to put a brand on your ass before we question you." "No, no, no!" they both said, "We are phonies working with two employees in the War Department in Washington, D.C."

Kling ands Zeke said, "You two are taking the enjoyment out of our jobs. We were going to hang both of you upside down, legs apart, and brand the letter "M" on you penis. Instead, we are going to turn you over to the U.S. Marshall who will have you transferred to Washington for trial. Now if things don't go right we will find you and use the branding iron." After checking out records and Indian conduct they left the reservation. The Crow Creek Indian Reservation was not on their list but they decided to check it out. Records were up to date and no trouble with Indian conduct so they headed to Kennebec to board the train east.

December 10, 1910 all hands were present at I.R.O.S. Headquarters. Colonel Dell Rico walked in and said, "At ease." He warmly greeted all hands, and then said, "I have bad news for you people. No Christmas leaves. New assignments. Captains Pikus and Wells to Haiti and Santo Domingo to form Armed Police Forces, a Constabulary. They will train Police and Civil Government employees. Captain Joseph Bryla and one hundred fifty Marines will accompany them. They will be stationed temporarily. Captains Pikus and Wells will return to I\.R.O.S. Headquarters by April 1, 1911. Colonel Byrnes and Captain Kling to Nicaragua to set up a Constabulary at two locations. Two hundred Marines will go with them. Byrnes and Kling to return to I.R.O.S. Headquarters on April 1, 1911. Captain Gary Conrad and the two hundred Marines will stay in Nicaragua until further notice. Master Sergeants Thomas Quick and Earl Murphy to assist Captain Conrad, Lt. Harry Bean and Warrant Officer Zeke to command I.R.O.S. Headquarters. Lieutenants Eckert and Sambach will go to Washington, D.C. Investigations War Department, Trail Preparation. Attestation of facts and events on an Indian Reservations. Colonel Byrnes and Captain Kling will board the Troop ship Harry Lee out of Norfolk, Va. December 19, 1911 at 1800 hours. Captain Pikus and Warrant Officer Wells will also board the Harry Lee on the same day and hour. Captains Bryla and Conrad, and Lt.Bean, Sgt.s Quick and Murphy will board with the Marines and equipment. Two days leave for

Colonel Byrnes, Captains Kling and Pikus, also Lts. Sambach and Eckert, Warrant Officers Wells and Zeke.

Byrnes, Kling, Pikus, and Wells to be at the train station Washington, D.C. track 2 December 14 at 0900 hours to board the train to Norfolk, Va. The two days leave was great. Pikus' and Kling's pregnant wives were so happy they were crying. Their children actually did not know their fathers, only what their mothers had told them.

December 19, 1910 the troop and supply ship Harry Lee was one of the small ships the Navy had hanging around since 1895. The ship was named after a Civil War General it accommodated a crew of one hundred Navy men and four hundred Marines. The food wasn't bad. The ship's usual run was the Caribbean Islands and South America. No escort was needed in peace time. The Harry Lee had a couple of guns on it and a gunner 2nd class Louis Byrnes. Now, Louie Byrnes was more or less a legend on Navy ships around the Caribbean. He shipped around the islands for fifteen years. The Navy kept him there. He was a good gunner's mate. They called him "One shot Louie". He also was named "Killer Louie". When on leave Louie always chased after rich widows. Some one said he married a girl from New Jersey and had two children. When Louie found out there was a Colonel Byrnes on board ship he asked his Captain for permission to speak to Colonel Byrnes. Permission was granted and Louie went to Colonel Byrnes' quarters. The outcome was Colonel Byrnes was Louie's cousin on his mother's side. Louie had heard he had a cousin in the Marines.

"O Happy Day!" The gods of war were with Louie. Colonel Byrnes told Louie that he was going to Nicaragua to set up a constabulary. He was also ordered to take a patrol out in the jungle and bring in Simon La Pue. La Pue was an insurgent and wanted by Nicaragua and the United States governments. He had killed two U.S. State Department employees. Louie asked Byrnes if he could go with the patrol. He knew Simon La Pue. Louie had a run into him at bars in the Caribbean Islands. "If your Captain gives his permission and you sign a waiver

I will take you with us. Since you know La Pue you will be an asset to the patrol. You could be assigned as a Corpsman. First I want to see you fire a .03-Springfield rifle and a .38 cal. revolver also, if you know how to throw a grenade and use a shot gun. If you get the Captain's permission I will meet you at the stern after we get underway tomorrow morning at 0900 hours. I will have a Gunnery Sergeant with me."

Colonel Byrnes said we were going to leave one hundred Marines at Puerto Cabezas with Captain Conrad in charge. Sergeant Quick will be second in command at the Constabulary. "I will take one hundred Marines to Blue Fields and start a Constabulary. Lt. Harry Bean will be in charge and his second in command will be Sergeant Murphy. Captain Kling and I will take Gunner Louie and twenty Marines out in the jungle to run down Simon La Pue. Last report on La Pue he was in the Blue Fields area. Every man on this patrol will carry ninety rounds of .30 cal. ammo, .03 SF rifle, .38 revolver, twenty-five rounds, bayonet, knife, canteen of water, first aid pack, clean socks, one pair extra field shoes, one blanket, one change of under wear, poncho, sanitary pack, and each man will have in his pack a five day supply of either canned beans, stew, or mutton and enough hard tack." We will also live off the land; bananas, melon, bread, fruit and, oranges. "It will be a hard and heavy trip. Don't forget your mosquito nets. The uniform will be the new green dungaree pants, shirts, and blouse, green dome hat. Each man will take care of his horse. Gunner Louie will be in charge of the pack mules and the machine gun and mortars. We will take rope, dynamite, sticks, fuses, caps, and some extra long machetes, also horse grain. Horses will be brushed daily."

Chapter 10

The Harry Lee moved out of Norfolk the 20th of December, 1910. It arrived at Puerto Cabezas, Nicaragua on December 25 Christmas Day at 1300 hours. A camp was already set up for the Marines tents, mess halls, and heads. Bully beef, potatoes, carrots, onions, and fresh baked bread with jelly. What a Christmas dinner! Four Marines said they found a keg of cerveza (beer). The day after Christmas a Nicaraguan barkeeper came around saying that someone stole a keg of cerveza.

Gunner mate Louie Byrnes who the Marines called "One shot Swabby Byrnes" asked if the Marines always ate like what we just ate. Sergeant Young said, "We eat better in the field. We have canned corned beef, stew, beans, sardines, fried plantains, and sometimes we catch some chickens and have a party. We also get canned milk for our coffee. Breakfast is usually a good meal; fried bacon, bacon fat cooked with hard tack, and canned beans with coffee, and sometimes a banana."

Three Nicaraguan Police Officers who were accused of cowardice in a fire fight with Simon La Pue approached the Marine camp at Blue Fields and asked to see the Commanding Officer. They had been fired from their jobs. They said, "We are not cowards." They had inferior weapons and the wrong ammunition. They wanted to redeem themselves. They knew the areas the Marines were covering and wanted to volunteer as scouts. Colonel Byrnes said he would check them out with his contacts. They checked out. The patrol was set to move out December 30th at 0900 hours. One Nicaraguan ex- Police officer on the right flank, one on the left, and the third one way out in front of the patrol. Captain Kling was also out front. All had shotguns for close jungle fighting. The Police officer on the left flank shot two men he said he had recognized them as La Pue's men. He saw them watching the camp and then following the patrol. Colonel Byrnes said, "Well done. We came here to catch La Pue, let's get him and get the hell out of here." The first night out one of the Marines on guard duty was killed. Some one crept up on him and cut his throat, then cut off his head, and disappeared with it. The next day his head was on a stick on the trail we were following. Colonel Byrnes did not have much experience with this kind of conduct. Captain Kling saw plenty. The patrol moved on.

The forward scout who was out about three quarters of a mile waited for Captain Kling to catch up. He knew Kling was behind him. He told Kling about five hundred yards ahead he saw about thirty armed men. He believed they were setting up an ambush where the trail crossed the main road. Kling told the scout to stay where he was. Kling went back to tell Colonel Byrnes. Byrnes and Kling worked out a plan. Twenty-four Marines would move as quietly as they could about one hundred and fifty yards closer twelve on the right flank and twelve on the left flank outside of the insurgents' perimeter. Gunner Louie and twelve Marines would take the machine gun and ammo and move to the rear of the ambush perimeter. "Our plan will only be completely effective if everyone moves and acts quietly until the mortar shells hit. Three Marines will stand by and take care of the horses and mules. The three scouts, Colonel Byrnes, Captain Kling, and the remaining three Marines will try to move within mortar range. One mortar shell will be shot to the north, south, east, and west, and one inside the insurgents' perimeter. Gunner Louie and his Marines with the machine gun should be able to knock off any of the insurgents running to the rear. The right and left flank Marines should get their share. Colonel Byrnes, Captain Kling, the three scouts, and eleven Marines will shoot any coming their way." The plan worked. When all shooting stopped fifteen insurgents were dead. The wounded were all shot – dead. Total twenty-five dead. The Marines casualties were one scout, one Marine on the right flank and one in the rear both dead, three with arm and leg wounds. Kling had the Marines move all the dead insurgents' bodies together. Colonel Byrnes marched off with all but three older Marines and Gunner Louie. Kling and the older Marines cut off all the testicles and penises of the insurgents. Kling wrapped the up in a poncho and called for one of the scouts to drop them off at the next barrio. Kling knew La Pue would get the message. Colonel Byrnes told three of the youngest Marines to wrap the dead Marines in ponchos. They were to take them and the three wounded back to the base camp on their horses. Gunner Louis said, "You Marines don't let any grass grow under your feet." He said after this patrol he would tell his mates to give the Marines lots of room. "Don't' get in their way. They love to cut."

The patrol moved on to Matagalpa. The advance scout reported Simon La Pue was holed up with about one hundred men outside of Ocotal. One of La Pue's troubles was xenophobia. Before leaving Matagalpa, Colonel Byrnes telegraphed home base at Blue Fields asking if a hundred Marines could be landed on the beach near Leon, Chinandega, or Managua. He said he was down to forty Marines and believed Simon La Pue had over three hundred insurgents. He could use a machine gun section, ammo, and two mortars -60-m.m. He would send one scout with Captain Kling to escort the Marines and weapons to Matagalpa the present patrol's position. The reply came back "can do." The 2nd squadron of the Pacific Home Fleet was on maneuvers about sixty miles off the coast of Managua, Nicaragua. "It may take three days to reach you. Stay at present position." Two days later one hundred Marines from the Battleship California were landed on the beach outside of Managua. Kling and one of the Police scouts met the one hundred Marines. The Captain in command was an old friend of Kling's. Kling's friend was Captain Moore an old drinking buddy. Pikus, Moore, and Kling met at the rifle range at Norfolk, Virginia eight years back. Moore was a Corporal then. Moore asked Kling if he had a brother in the Navy. He said an Officer by the name of Frank Kling was in command of a Gunnery Section on the Battleship Oregon he was a First Lieutenant. Kling said some years back he received a letter from his brother informing him about his father and mother who died in a house fire. His brother mentioned he was going in the Navy.

A day and a half later the Byrnes patrol grew to one hundred and eighteen Marines. The Marines counted Louie as a Marine. Louie was sorry he ever left his ship. The mosquitoes, bugs, bad water, always feeling dirty, and people shooting at you night and day was not Louie's cut of tea. It was now January 20, 1911, the Marines told Louie if he didn't get killed he could be back on his ship by March 25, 1911. To make Louie's problems worse he had his pants down trying to defecate and a shot rang out from the jungle. The bullet creased Louie's behind. The crease wasn't serious but Louie said it hurt like hell. When the Marines looked at Louie they had a smile on their faces. Louie said, "Where do these boys come from? What kind of training makes Marines? They live awful in the field; they are respectful, disciplined, yet kind and caring. They fight like wildcats and fight amongst themselves, but let anyone hurt a Marine and the whole Corps will jump on him. They can't wait to get in a fight and shoot their rifles. They don't seem to fear death. When one gets killed they say he is guarding the streets of heaven." Louie said, "I believe the Lord made the Marines the best fighting men of the world." The Marines liked Louie and had a lot of respect for him after the last battle. He was a terror with the machine gun, but a Navy man cleaning horses and mules! When he gets back to his ship his mates will never believe him.

Captain Kling, the two scouts, and four of the older Marines went ahead of the main group to look for snipers. They found plenty in the trees, bushes, and ground holes. Kling's left leg got creased the second time in his career. One of the scouts was shot in the right arm but not too serious. The main group was a mile outside the barrio of Ocotal. From a hill Colonel Byrnes looked over the insurgents' fortifications. He said, "What a joke!" In the rear of the fortification was a river with a dock and a lot of little boats. The insurgents were behind rocks, in trees, in holes, and two or three buildings. They chased the inhabitants out of the town. The Marines had a lot of sniper fire. They lost eight men. Within range Byrnes had the three mortars fire. They destroyed the dock, most of the boats, and the three buildings. Byrnes' machine gunner killed a lot of insurgents on the left and right flanks. Louie had a field day. The main body of Marines moved forward to wipe out the insurgents. The Marines were shooting in holes, trees, behind logs. They killed many. Some wanted to surrender. Kling had them shot. No prisoners. He did not want these people alive to kill later. Thirty Marines were killed and twenty-five wounded. Byrnes had about seventy-two able bodied Marines. Simon La Pue had escaped. Many of the insurgents' weapons, ammo, and supplies had to be destroyed. The trail back to Matagalpa had many problems. Twenty Marines died of their wounds. Byrnes telegraphed Captain Conrad at the Constabulary in Blue Fields. Byrnes and his Marines were on the way back when unfortunately six more Marines were killed by sniper fire. Byrnes came in with seventy walking Marines including Louie.

Most of the horses and mules were killed. Colonel Byrnes did not set up a second Constabulary at Matagalpa. He had one hundred seventy-two Marines. Since Simon La Pue got away Byrnes didn't want to leave so few Marines there to be slaughtered. Matagalpa was too far away for the Constabulary at Blue Fields should they be attacked by a large force of insurgents. Simon La Pue would love to slaughter a small Marine force. He may still have two to three hundred followers. Anyway, Byrnes didn't have enough ammo and equipment. Gunner Louie asked Colonel Byrnes when he believed they would be relieved. Byrnes said about March 24th. It was now February 10, 1911. Captain Kling asked Louie how his behind was. Louie said, "I have a red mark to prove I was wounded." Louie's job until relieved was to train all the Marines at the Constabulary on how to use and break down the machine gun also, some Nicaraguan recruits who wanted to be soldiers. Louie was as happy as a fish in water teaching Marines how to use a gun!

Captain Conrad, Sergeants Quick and Murphy were told

they would be in charge of the Constabulary when Byrnes and Kling were relieved by orders from headquarters, Washington. Captain Pikus, Warrant Officer Wells, and seventy-five Marines were landed at Port de Pais, Haiti to set up a Constabulary. Captain Joseph Bryla and seventy-five Marines were landed at Santiago, Santo Domingo. They set up a Constabulary and started recruiting men. Captain Bryla was told by Washington he would be at Santo Domingo for at least a year. At Port de Pais, Haiti Captain Pikus and Warrant Officer Wells had problems. After landing and looking over the area set up for the Constabulary Pikus said, "No way!" There was no water or sewerage; it was half swamp with snakes and mosquitoes, an infectious area. Pikus quartered and fed his Marines on the beach. Two local government men came forward and had their hands out. Pikus said, "Keep them out." He called two of his Sergeants and Wells to show the government men how a Marine can use a machete. The two government men ran like hell away from Wells and the Sergeants who were swinging the machetes. Before darkness set in a government agent approached Pikus and said he would show them an area for the Marine Captain's approval. Pikus said the area was satisfactory. His Marines set up tents and the Constabulary started to take form. The next day he told Wells to send out two patrols of twelve Marines and patrol out about twenty-five miles from the new Constabulary north, south, east, and west. The patrols were to be equipped for five days. No hostilities were reported in Pikus' or Captain Bryla's areas.

Two women stopped at the Blue Fields number one sentry post. They told the Sergeant they had information for Colonel Byrnes. They were both searched and the Sergeant in charge took them to Colonel Byrnes' quarters. They told the Colonel that Simon La Pue and ten men were staying at a small casa in Ciego. Ciego was a small barrio about a mile from the Constabulary. These people must be the ones taking shots at the Marines sometimes early in the morning and late at night. Colonel Byrnes called for Captain Kling and asked him if he wanted the pleasure. Kling took one Sergeant and ten Marines, rifles, revolvers, and twenty Mills hand grenades. He also took along one of the women in case of a trap. It was near twilight when Kling's Marines crept out of the jungle at the rear of the casa. Kling told two Marines to go to the right and two to the left. He crept around to the front with the Sergeant and the other six Marines. Two male persons came out of the casa walked a few feet away took out their penises and muddied the ground. Both had rifles on their shoulders. Kling's loud voice said, "Simon

Come out with your hands up." The two men relieving themselves started to take their rifles from their shoulders were dead on the ground in seconds. Simon and two men came out shooting. Kling and his Marines put more holes in them. Then a fish net. Grenades were thrown. Five men and one woman were dead. The casa completely destroyed. Hostilities ceased in the areas. Byrnes, Kling, the Sergeants, and Louie continued to train state, government, and local police military fashion.

March 18, 1911 Captain Pikus and Warrant officer Wells were notified to be at Port de Pais dockside at 0900 hours for pick up by the Harry Lee. Colonel Byrnes, Captain Kling, and Gunner Louie were also notified to be at dockside Blue Fields 1300 hours March 22nd. Everything worked well on the pickups to return to Norfolk, Virginia. Gunner Louie couldn't wait to tell his shipmates of the action he saw with the Marines. There were some Marines on the ship going back to the States from other areas. Colonel Byrnes had six Marines with rifles line up across from Gunner Louie with the ship's Captain and two of Louie's mates. They fired a Six Volley Rifle Salute for Louie's service with the Marines. Byrnes said when he returned to Quantico he would put Louie in for a Marine Nicaraguan Campaign and Bravery Medal. Louie had a tear in his eye. Colonel Byrnes, Captains Pikus, Kling, and Warrant Officer Wells were back at I.R.O.S. Headquarters March 28, 1911. First thing Byrnes, Pikus, and Kling did was telephone their wives.

Chapter 11

March 29, 1911 at 0900 hours Colonel Dell Rico stopped at the Intelligence Resources Operation Specialist (I.R.O.S.) Headquarters at Quantico, Virginia. He gave Colonel Byrnes a furlough sheet. A ten day furlough for Colonel Byrnes, Captains Kling and Pikus, Warrant Officers Wells and Zeke, and Lts. Sambach and Eckert. All are to report back at I.R.O.S. Headquarters April 12, 1911 at 1300 hours. Officers returning are to report to sick bay for a physical and mental examination April 13th and 14th. All furloughed Officers from I.R.O.S. must qualify for reassignments.

A meeting was called for 0900 hours April 15th by Colonel Byrnes. Dated 13th April, 1911 Department of Defense Secretary of the Navy – 1001-7-to Marine Corps Commandant John L. Smith Washington, D.C. Promotions; Captain Walter Kling to Major USMC, Captain Edward Pikus to Major USMC. By special Act of Congress H-12-11 to Secretary of the Navy, Marine Corps Commandant; Warrant Officers Zeke and Wells have distinguished themselves for eight years. Meritous Conduct – Personal Danger, Voluntary Risk of Life, Conflict with Armed Enemies, and Heroic Service Saving Lives. The Marine Corps needs leaders of their caliber. Pikus said to Kling, "Wells and Zeke wanted to stay Warrant Officers. It gave them more freedom with the enlisted Marines." Kling said, "The Marine Corps needs more combat experienced Captains, these two Marines have it." Colonel Byrnes said the following assignments came directly from the Commandant Office Washington, D.C. All Officers and enlisted Marines at I.R.O.S. must qualify with the .45 caliber-1911 Colt Pistol and03-Springfield Rifle also, the Colt Model 1895-3 -03 Browning, 1904 maxim Machine guns, bayonet, and hand grenade course. I.R.O.S. Marines must qualify within the two months allowance time.

June 2, 1911 all I.R.O.S. Officers were called to a meeting at headquarters. Colonel Dell Rico and a Lieutenant General named Henry P. Osman from the Logistics Command USMC were with him. General Osman said the Marine Corps has grown. We now have one thousand officers and thirteen thousand enlisted Marines. A meeting of the War Department is scheduled June 15 at 0900 hours. The Secretary of the Army, Navy, and the Marine Commandant will officiate. All I.R.O.S. Officers are to bring all documentations and notes they have of their travels. This is a Naval Secret Commission. Present will be four U.S. Navy Admirals, four U.S. Army Generals, and the Commandant of the Marine Corps with his eight top Marine I.R.O.S. Officers. The meeting was held as scheduled. The subject was Marine Security of U.S. possessions and protectorates. The War Department Secretary of the Navy came up with the following:

Plan 1 – Deployment of Marines

Pacific Fleet:
    10 Battleships – 1000 Marines
    3 Heavy Cruisers – 225 Marines
    2 Light Cruisers – 150 Marines
    15 Destroyers
    2 Mine Layers
    2 Mine Sweepers
    6 Coast guard Vessels
Miscellaneous auxiliaries:
    8 coaling – 2 oiler Ships
    5 Transport and supply Ships
    6 Ammunition Ships

Naval Bases:
    Pear Harbor Naval Shipyard
    1st Defense Company – 250 Combat Ready Marines with rifles, machine guns, mortars, and Engineer Squads
    Coast Defense, Army Artillery Field Guns 3 inch caliber, Naval 3 and 5 inch

    Subic Bay Naval Station
    2nd Marine Defense Company

300 Combat Ready Marines
Station Security

Guam
3rd Marine Defense – Security
200 Combat Ready Marines
Naval Coaling Station

Wake Island
4th Marine Defense – Security
150 Marines

Midway Island
5th Defense – Security
150 Marines
Naval Coaling Station

American Samoa (Tututile) Pago Pago
6th Marine Defense – Security
150 Marines
Coaling Station

Hawaii – Kaneohe Bay
200 Base Security
4th USMC Regiment 1200 Marines (support for trouble areas)

State of Washington
Sandpoint Naval Station – Security- 60 Marines
Puget Sound shipyard – 100 Marines
Bremerton Naval Barrack – 6 Marines

California
Naval Base Coronado –Security-150 Marines
Naval Repair
San Diego Naval Base – 300 Marines
USMC Base Training Personnel-500 Marines

1st Guard Company – Security-100 Marines
2nd Guard Company – Security-100 Marines
1st Regiment – 1500 Trained Combat Marines
Approximately 6200 Marines WD, SN – recommendation.

Please mark your sheet with comments to the Secretary of the Navy with your recommendations and changes in present plans. Sign your comment sheets. Turn them in before you leave.

Atlantic Ocean and Caribbean Sea Fleet:
    10 Battleships – 1000 Marines
    2 Heavy Cruisers – 200 Marines
    1 Light Cruiser – 50 Marines
    20 Destroyers
    2 Mine Sweepers
    2 Mine Layers
    6 Coal and Oilers
    5 Transport and Supply Ships
    6 Ammunition Ships
Miscellaneous Auxiliaries-Ships

Naval Bases:
    Rhode Island
    Newport Naval Base
    200 Marine- Security

    Connecticut
    New London Naval Base
    Base Security-75 Marines

    New York
    Brooklyn Naval Yard
    60 Marines

    New Jersey
    Lakehurst Naval Station

80 Marines

Pennsylvania
U.S. Naval Shipyard
75 Marines

Maryland
U.S. Naval Academy
Instructors-25 Marines

Virginia
Norfolk naval Station
Security-75 Marines
Norfolk shipyard
75 Marines
Quantico Marine Reservations
1st Guard Company-75 Marines
2nd Guard company-75 Marines
Training Battalin-400 Marines
Logistics, Motor Pool - I.R.O.S.-200 Marines
Maintenance Armory-200 Marines
Marine Corps School-65 Marines
Officers Training-120 Marines
1st Regiment - 1st Division-220 Marines

Washington, D.C.
Marine Barracks-75 Marines
Marine Band-75 Marines

South Carolina
Naval Weapons Station-75 Marines
Parris Island Training Center-900 Marines

Georgia
King Bay Naval Base-60 Marines
Marine Corps Logistics-60 Marines

Florida
Jackson Naval Station-70 Marines
May Port Naval Station-60 Marines
Pensacola NAS-60 Marines

Louisiana
New Orleans Naval A.S. – Security-60 Marines

Puerto Rico
Marine Barrack San Juan – Security-100 Marines
Naval Station- 60 Marines

Constabularies:
   Nicaragua – Security-120 Marines
   Haiti-120 Marines
   Santo Domingo-120 Marines

   Cuba
   Guantanamo Bay Navy – Marine Barrack-200 Marines

   Panama
   Colon-100 Marines

Approximately six thousand three hundred (6300) Marines.

After three days living at the Marine Barracks in Washington, D.C. the seven I.R.O.S. Officers were ready to leave. The three days of discussions with Marine General Officers, the Secretary of the Navy, and the Commandant of the Marine Corps was starting to get tiring. The I.R.O.S. Officers were active field officers. No doubt the Secretary of the Navy and the Commandant will see things their way. One thing the I.R.O.S. Officers stated was NO POLITICS in or for the Marine Corps. The Marines will not have politicians policing, interrupting, or interfering with their duties or assignments. When one is qualified to be a Marine he has sold his body and soul to his God, Corps, and Country for the term of his enlistment. The I.R.O.S. Officers say one should look and inquire about the Marines (kill or be killed) before enlisting. There are only four ways to get out of the Corps in 1911; 1) to get killed or die 2) wounded and unable to serve 3) end of your enlistment 4) desertion. Desertion is usually a General Court Martial with death by firing squad immediately after conviction and loss of all benefits and a pauper's grave.

I.R.O.S. Officers are to return to I.R.O.S. Headquarters no later than June 22, 1911 at 0900 hours for reassignment. Colonel Dell Rico telephoned Majors Pikus and Kling at I.R.O.S. Headquarter at 0900 hours on June 24, 1911. "Commandant Smith would like you people to draw a Table of Organization for an Attack Battalion. When completed send the original copy by runner to the Commandant's Office marked Attention: Colonel Dell Rico." Pikus said, "I guess we have to help the big boys."

Year 1911 - Attack Battalion
Commanding Officer – Rank Colonel or Major
(Numeral indicates number of Marines)
Liaison to Commanding Officer: 2- Majors, 3- Captains, 2-1st Lieutenants, 2 2nd Lieutenants
8-Company Clerks, 2-Sergeants, 2-Corporals, 3-Privates
Communication: 1-Master Sergeant, 1-1st Sergeant, 2-Warrant Officers, 2-Gunnery Sergeants, 4-Grave Registration Sergeants
20-Wagon Masters or Pool Drivers, 6- Ambulance, 10-Corporals,
5-Sergeants, 5-Privates (may also serve as riflemen)
8-Maintenance – Wire Communication (may also serve as riflemen)
4-Supply Sergeants, 4-Assistants (may also serve as riflemen)
8-Mess Sergeants, 10-Cooks-Sergeants, 10 Assistant Cooks (all will serve as riflemen when needed)
4-Ammunition Sergeants, 4-Corporals, 4-Privates
8-Inner circle Guards-Officers-Clerks, 4-Corporals, 4-

Privates
20-Perimeter Headquarters Guards
Individual Military Equipment Office
H Company approximately 142 Marines

A – Company	B – Company
1-Captain	1-Captain
1-Lieutenant	1-Lieutenant
1-Gunnery Sgt.	1-Gunnery Sgt.
1-1st Sgt.	1-1st Sgt.
1st Platoon	1st Platoon
2-Platoon Sgts.	2-Platoon Sgts.
8-Buck Sgts.	8-Buck Sgts.
16-Corporals	16-Corporals
100-Riflemen	100-Riflemen
6-.30cal. Machine Guns	6-.30cal. Machine Guns
2nd Platoon	2nd Platoon
7-60mm Mortars-21 Marines	7-60mm Mortars-21 Marines
3-Engineers Demolition	3-Engineers Demolition
6-New 37mm-Fieldguns	6-New 37mm Fieldguns
18-Marines	18-Marines
Canisters, Ball, Metal Shot	Canisters, Ball, Metal Shot
3-Communications Marines	3-Communications Marines
3rd Platoon	3rd Platoon
14—Riflemen	14-Riflemen
1-Buck Sgt., 2-Corporals	1-Buck Sgt., 2-Corporals
15-Wagons, Horses, or	15-Wagons, Horses, or
5-Motor Pool Trucks	5-Motor Pool Trucks
5-Sgts., 5-Corporals, 5-Privates	5-Sgts., 5-Corporals, 5-Privates
Ammo – Food – Equipment	Ammo – Food – Equipment
Total 227 Marines	Total 227 Marines

Artillery

4 Pack 75mm Howitzers-20Marines
or Carrona Des – Gun Carriages
(includes Ammo – Carriers – Wagons or Motor)
12 Marines, 81mm Motors-4
8-Sts., 16-Corporals, 28-Privates
20-Riflemen, 6-Communications, Transportation

Medical
3-Doctors, 10-Assist. Corpsmen
3-Communications, 15-Male Nurses
25-Field Corpsmen attached to Combat Companies

Total Attack Battalion – 728 Marines
717 Marines
9 Officers
2 Warrant Officers

June 30, 1911 twenty-three hundred hours Colonel
Dell Rico telephoned the Sergeant of the Guard at I.R.O.S.
Headquarters to notify Majors Kling and Pikus, Captains
Zeke and Wells, Lts. Eckert and Sambach to report to the
Commandant's office on July 2 at 0900 hours. All these Officers
were on over night leave. All the Officers notified were in the
meeting room at the Commandant's Headquarters on time.
Colonel Dell Rico was fifteen minutes late which he blamed
on traffic. He loved his new Ford. Some car thirty-five miles
an hour. Commandant Smith walked in at 0930 hours. He
warmly greeted his I.R.O.S. Officers and had his attendants
pass out coffee and muffins. "Gentlemen," the Commandant
said, "We have been asked again by the President and the
State Department for help. Before I tell you their problems
I will tell you our problem. The I.R.O.S. at Quantico will be
out of business by the end of this year. The Navy Intelligence
Department is taking over but not all. Our Marine eight man
Special Unit will survive. We are what I believe are the forerunners of the Central Intelligence Agency of our country.
Your headquarters will be in Washington, D.C. You people

will have a building with offices and sleeping quarters. Your Marines will mess with the I&R Marines. Officers will mess at the Officers Club. Your unit will be called Installations and Logistics Resources Program for the Commandant (ILRP). Pick your best First Sergeant and twelve Guard Marines, no lower in rank than Corporal. Three Marine clerks and three map readers, code communication Marines. Guard duty three shifts daily 365 days. The guard will also take care of maintenance and Police call. Only qualified Marines. Your headquarters are not open to anyone. Permission can only be granted by the Commandant or Colonel Dell Rico. Re-screen the Marines you pick. They are not to reveal their duties to anyone. When asked they are to say we work on Marine Logistics. The President and State Department are asking our unit to go into Mexico on a rescue mission. I am asking you eight Marines who have been with me for almost ten years; do we help out or let the State Department pay? The bandits kidnapped two State Department employees and one American businessman. They want five hundred thousand in gold or a train box car loaded with weapons. There is a possibility of a rescue attempt. The State Department has three Mexican brothers who are business men on their payroll. They are associated with most of the bandits in Mexico (go betweens). Real thieves themselves. Do we volunteer?" All eight Marines volunteered. "You people know the routine. Six of you will go to Mexico. Majors Kling and Pikus, Captains Zeke and Wells, Lts. Eckert and Sambach. Long hair, don't shave, dirty and ragged looking clothes. You will be traveling by horses most of the time. Look you files over. Take the same type of equipment you took on the Indian Reservation investigations. Make sure you take Mills hand grenades. You people will leave on July 9. You will meet your first contact at Chihuahua, Mexico at a business house called Comedere no later than July 27th. Go in the back door of the business house. The bandit kidnappers we believe have about four hundred men. They want the money or weapons no later than August 15th. The go betweens are at Chihuahua. We believe the hostages are somewhere within a five mile radius of Chihuahua. Lts. Eckert and Sambach will travel west then south from El Paso to Ciudad Guerrero and then to Chihuahua. For any information they will telephone or telegraph Colonel Byrnes who will have a receiving office at El Paso. The code is I.L.A.P. Unit KZ-PW-ES. All orders or changes will come from Colonel Byrnes. The banditos call themselves El Cuchillos. Pikus and Wells will travel east then south to Aldama and then to Chihuahua. They also will be on the look out for the El Cuchillos. Kling and Zeke will travel south from El Paso to El Sauz then to Chihuahua." The Commandant said to watch out for the Mexican federal soldiers. "I will bet a dollar to a donut the hostages are held at Aldama. Take all the weapons, ammo, and equipment you need. I want all of you back alive. God Bless You!"

On July 4, 1911 Second Lieutenant USMC Thomas A. Smith was killed while on patrol outside of Bluefields, Nicaragua. He was Commandant Smith's son aged twenty-four. Colonels Dell Rico and Byrnes, Majors Kling and Pikus, Captains Wells and Zeke, and Lts. Eckert and Sambach expressed their condolences to the Commandant and his wife at their private residence. The Commandant said, "I lost my son, but I have eight more. You people have always been my sons." They were all given a two day leave. They were also told by Colonel Dell Rico if they met any opposition they were to say they were going to join the Revolution, Pancho Villa's or Zapatista – or deep six the opposition.

"Watch out for Federalist Troopers at Ciudad, Guerrero," Eckert telegraphed Colonel Byrnes. After checking out areas and information the El Cuchillos' headquarters were at Aldama outside of Chihuahua. Eckert and Sambach were going to the meeting place at Chihuahua. Kling's and Pikus' unit had no trouble and from information they received they were also going to the meeting place at Chihuahua. Colonel Byrnes returned a telegram, "Go get them!" On July 26th the three I.R.O.S. units met the contact at 0930 hours at the business house called the Comedere Provision Co. The contact said the hostages were being held at Los Cantina Casa in Aldama, the headquarters for the El Cuchillos. The village of Aldama had a population of about four hundred people. It was a wine making village. Two hundred of them were revolutionist El Cuhillos. There were no police or any Federalist Troops around. In fact while traveling their units told the people who said they were happy that they were joining the Revolution. The people would warn the units and tell them where the Police and troops were. Major Kling asked the contact how he knew the hostages were at the house in Aldama. He said he saw them there the day before while he was at the house. He delivered provisions and blankets. He said El Lobo (the wolf) was calling in all Cuchillos.

"El Lobo is the leader of the bandits, his name is Juan Provilla Sona. He claims to be the cousin of Pancho Villa. The house sets off the road about fifty yards. They have an old Gatling gun with little ammunition covering the road and front of the house." The contact said about twelve men guard the house day and night. The hostages are escorted to the out houses (toilets). Two guards to each hostage. "I am surprised they haven't raped the women hostage. The rest of the El Cuchillos are out getting drunk day and night at the winery or playing around with the town women." Pikus said, "It doesn't appear tough. The only problem will be the rear guard." Major Kling said, "The last communication with Colonel Byrnes said the Commandant was sticking his neck out for us. Byrnes said on the road the Mexicans call Road 45 from El Sueco to Chihuahua the Commandant has twenty-four Marines dressed like tramps looking for and wanting to join the Revolution. They travel two to three Marines a quarter of a mile apart. They are the Spanish speaking Marines you people trained from I.R.O.S. They have horses, weapons, and plenty of ammo. The pass word is I.R.O.S. They are all volunteers including their officers, Captains Lester Puller and Hank Halphen. They have with them one 60mm mortars with eight rounds. Do not leave anything to identify Americans."

Pikus said, "Let us see how they change guards." The

contact said he heard the guards were twelve hours on duty then off to the girls and winery. The guards he said were lazy always half drunk. El Lobo most of the time was in Chihuahua with his Lieutenants and whores. Aldama is five miles from Chihuahua. All the bandits know the value of the hostages. El Lobo's day and night Sergeants and a couple of guards take their job seriously. The night guards walk up the hill from the winery in twos or three at a time. Pikus and Kling watched the changing of the guards for one night. Pikus said, "We grab six of their men walking toward the house fifteen minutes before the guards are relieved. Deep six them! We tell the Sargento (sergeant) malo cabra carne (bad goat meat), disenteria. Eckert and Sambach will be about sixty feet from the front of the house, Zeke and Wells about forty feet. Take your time do a good job." Kling said, "Pikus and I will be about seventy feet from the front or sides of the house. Pull them in the bush, garrote them or use you knives – no shooting. Put the act on. Tell the Sergeant the first day in camp no time to drink wine and they are put on guard duty. Don't over do it! You people look the part and speak their dialect. Let us try to do this quietly." Everything was working. The Sergeant fell for the dysentery story. He said he had it two weeks ago. Eckert and Sanbach had the outside guard duty walking around the house. They deep sixed the three guards on the Gatling gun. Eckert told them one by one he had a girl in the bush. They couldn't wait to get killed. Kling, Pikus, Wells, and Zeke went into the house. They deep sixed the Sergeant and three inside guards. The hostages were freed from the room they were locked in. Kling told Zeke and Eckert to get the hostages on horses or in a wagon and take off north on Road 45. Move fast and keep going until they see men with white cloth two inch head bands around their sombreros. They should be the Marine Rear Guard. Kling and Pikus set booby traps in the room. They had ammo and dynamite. They set string booby traps with hand grenades. The bandits had plenty of them. It was a good thing the bandits kept saddle horses outside the house day and night. Now the day before the people who owned the winery told the contact the bandits did not pay for anything. "They just take wine or women." The contact said they owed him plenty of money too. He was sure he wouldn't get paid. The bandits say, "For the Revolution." So, these people dispatched a runner to the Federalist Troopers who were on their way to Serdan. They told the soldiers the wine was free and maybe some money could come their way. They wanted the troopers to drive the bandits out of Aldama anyway they could.

Zeke and Eckert met with the Marine Rear Guard about fifteen miles north. Kling, Pikus, Wells, and Sambach were not too far behind them. They were traveling fast. It was a good thing they had extra horses. They thought they heard an explosion. It was now 0200 hours July 29, 1911. They did not meet any Federal Troops or opposition on their way back to El Paso. Most Federal Troops were around Mexico City and to the south fighting the Revolutionists. The State Department people were waiting for the hostages. They thanked the Marines. The Marines saddled up and headed northeast toward Dallas where transportation by train took them most of the way back to the I.R.O.S. headquarters at Quantico, Va. Pikus said, "Amen!" It was August 4, 1911.

Chapter 12

The Commandant gave the thirty-two Marines who participated in the Mexican Rescue a fifteen day furlough. Marines of this era and especially the Officers of I.R.O.S. would "Deep six" any corruptible people who approached them (by accident-naturally!). They would risk their lives for the good and welfare of their country. They did not like the politicians who interfered with the Marine Corps training. Some of the old Officers who did not know their "ass from a hole in the ground" unsuccessfully tried to disband the Marine Corps. The War Department Secretary of the Navy said, "They are here to stay." The State Department gave a dinner for the thirty-two rescuers. All enlisted Marines were promoted one stripe. All the I.R.O.S. Marines who were furloughed were told to report back for duty on August 24 at 1300 hours. Colonel Byrnes, Majors Kling and Pikus had a good time with their wives and children who hardly knew their fathers. Colonel Byrnes drove Kling and Pikus down to Quantico in his new Ford, 1912 Model.

Assignments were already posted at I.R.O.S. Headquarters. Colonel Byrnes and Lieutenant Thomas were assigned to I.R.O.S. Headquarters until disbandment December 15th 1911. They would receive a Christmas leave until January 3, 1912 and then report for duty to I.L.R.P. (Installation and Logistics, Resources Program) Headquarters in Washington, D.C. Major Kling, Captain Zeke, and Lt. Eckert will train and be in training with Company A, 1st Battalion, 1st Regiment. Major Pikus, Captain Wells, and Lt. Sambach will train and be in training with Company B, 1st Battalion, and 1st Regiment

So, four months passed. Christmas leaves were enjoyed and all had good times with their wives, children, and friends, and lots of snow. January 3, 1912 Kling, Pikus, Wells, Zeke, Eckert, and Sambach were at their new I.L.R.P. Headquarters waiting for Colonel Byrnes and Colonel Dell Rico. Guess whose car got stuck in the snow? "You guessed it!" Colonel Dell Rico's new Ford. The Officers told him to get a horse.

He said laughing, "Marines have I got good news for you. A Caribbean vacation!" Pikus said, "Lord did you forget us?" It appeared a Central American country was not paying their bills on time. They were killing our citizens, stealing our mail, and destroying property. The seven I.L.R.P. Officers said, "Boy we are sick of that place." Wells said, "This time let's really settle their hash." Colonel Byrnes in command of the 1st Battalion, 1st Regiment. Major Kling Company A with Captain Zeke, Lt. Eckert, 250 Marines and equipment to land at Blue Fields, Nicaragua January 21st. Major Pikus Company B with Captain Wells, Lt. Sambach, 250 Marines, and equipment to land at Puerto Cabezas January 17th. Major Johnson D Company 1st Battalion from San Diego with Captain Butler and Lt. Powell, 250 Marines, and equipment to land at Chinandega, Nicaragua on January 24, 1912. Company D will land from the Battleships Oregon and California on the Pacific coast near Chinandega. Twenty-five Marines from the Constabulary at Blue Fields will be relieved and transferred to Key West Soldier and Naval Hospital. Major Kling will replace them from his company. The mosquitoes, bugs, rain, filth, and diseases haven't changed. Malaria (paludismo) was no stranger to the Marines down there.

Admiral James S. Spiak – Caribbean Command
Re: NN105 – Admiral John Samel Commanding Officer
January 15, 1912
Guantanamo Bay Naval Base, Cuba
Navy Department, Washington, D.C.
Subject A: Promotion
Your Command Lieutenant Frank E. Kling to Lieutenant Commander
Effective January 17, 1912
Lieutenant Commander Kling has finished 1st in Destroyer Command School Norfolk, Va. He has passed the Destroyer Construction Examination.
Subject B:
Lieutenant Commander Kling shall take command DD-385

Destroyer Richey immediately. Now at your port.
Subject C:
Replacement- DD Experience, Naval repair, machine, and maintenance personnel. Medical and death casualties (yellow fever), malaria, ringworm, pheumation, fibrosis, advanced gonorrhea, expiration of enlistment shall be relieved.
Subject D:
The USS Harry Lee now transferred will be used as a hospital ship to relieve and transport casualties to Key West, Florida Soldiers and Naval Hospital for disposition. Also, to relieve San Juan, Puerto Rico Marine Barracks twenty-five Marines and twenty Naval casualties on or before the 19th and 20th of January 1912. Also to be relieved 10 Constabulary Marines, 12 Naval personnel casualties from Port de Plax, Haiti on or about January 23, 1912 15 Marines and 14 Naval personnel Constabulary casualties from Puerto Plata, Dominican Republic (Santo Domingo). These Marines will also be relieved 25 Marines and 30 Naval casualties from Blue Fields, Nicaragua January 26, 1912.
U.S. Navy pack, Reg 16-refer. 105

Navy Department
Secretary John Dillon
Washington, D.C.

To: Admiral Michael Paterson
USN Fleet Base-Building O
Norfolk, Virginia
January 10, 1912

Subject 1: Replacement Naval Personnel -Caribbean Command
 Re: Navy- Ref., 105- D146- R105
Subject 2: USS Merrill, Troop and Supply Ship to be outfitted with
500 Marines and equipment
125 Navy personnel and equipment

Subject 3: Ship to leave port no later than January 22, 1912 0900 hours

Subject 4: First stop Port de Plax, Haiti Constabulary – supplies

20 Marines

15 Navy personnel

Subject 5: Dominican Republic – supplies

30 Marines

35 Navy personnel

Subject 6: Marine Barracks San Juan, Puerto Rico

50 Marines

25 Navy personnel and supplies

Subject 7: Blue Fields, Nicaragua

225 Marines

40 Navy personnel

Ammunition, weapons, parts, field rations, tents, mosquito netting, telegraph equipment

10 horses and feed

Subject 8: Puerto Cabazon, Nicaragua

200 Marines

10 Navy personnel

Ammunition, weapons, parts, field rations, blankets, mosquito netting, telegraph equipment

10 horses and feed.

Two weeks work and the Constabulary and Marine camp was livable at Blue Fields. Mosquitoes, bugs, bad water, rain, and occasionally sniper fire day and night. Marines on off time would go out and try to nail the snipers. They did capture some. Took their equipment and guns then hung them up by the neck to dry. Colonel Byrnes was walking out of the door of his office at the Constabulary when he bent forward and downward to pick up the pencil he had dropped two bullets hit the frame of the door. He dropped to the floor and started crawling back into his office. His guards heard the shots and ran to the position they thought the shots were fired from. No one was around. That night Colonel Byrnes, Major Kling, Captain Zeke, and Lt. Eckert worked out a perimeter plan. The next day at twilight four squads of twelve Marines each with shotguns, 03 Springfield Rifles, hand grenades, smoke grenades, two 60mm mortars, twelve mortars, shells, 46 Marines, and four corpsmen (fifty in all) walked three miles outside of camp and formed a circular perimeter within ear shot. They laid low to the ground and were quiet. The mosquitoes didn't help. The Colonel said that before the squads went out his contacts reported that every night at least twenty-five insurgent bandits came close to the camp with a desire to get off a shot and kill a Marine. Around sunrise they observed guard positions and the number of men, weapons, and equipment we have. Tonight is a dark night. The Marines had put out about twenty-five trip wire traps, smoke and fragmentation grenades in the area they thought the insurgents would travel. About twenty-four hundred hours a loud talking group of men walked right into the trap lines. There were explosions to the left, explosions in the middle and right. White smoke grenades were going off. Two mortars had been setup. Their retreat was helped with mortar fire fifty yards in their direction. At day light twenty-five dead men and two women were found. Our contacts said, "That stopped the sniping and observing for now."

January 27, 1912 – Communications-
Lieutenant Commander Frank Kling
USS Richey-DD-385-Destroyer
To: Colonel Byrnes USMC-ILRP-Constabulary Blue Fields Major Pikus USMC-Puerto Cabezas, Nicaragua Coastal patrols by Destroyers Richey, Bolls, Day, and Smith Twelve Marine landing parties on each destroyer for emergencies Patrols from Gracias a Dios to San Juan Del Norte should assistance be needed Code word – ILRP - Say hello to Major L.C. Kling, DO 385-1/27/12 0930.

It is necessary to have Naval Coastal patrols on the Pacific Ocean coast as well as the Caribbean Sea Coast. For years now our country had been keeping its eye on three European

101

countries that had been favoring intervention with Nicaragua. Our Naval patrols were to stop and hold any ships that had weapons, ammunition, or military equipment for Nicaragua. The three DD-Destroyers patrolling the Pacific coast were Sim-384, Porter-271, and Barton-251. Major Johnson - D Company - Chinandega communicated with Lt. Commander Kling and Colonel Byrnes. On January 26, 1912 Major Johnson had his troops of D-Company settled in at Chinandega not too far from Leon. On January 27th at 0700 hours Johnson's troops were at breakfast when all hell broke out. His perimeter guards and machine guns went into action. He was under attack by many insurgents. His Marines quickly managed defensive positions. The 37mm Fieldgun with canister shot and the machine guns did a job on the insurgents. When the attack stopped one hundred and twenty-five insurgents were dead and twenty were wounded. After interrogation they were shot. "Kill or be killed." D-Company was not going to let the wounded insurgents get well to kill another day. Twenty-two Marines were dead and twenty-eight wounded. On January 28th two hundred Marines were landed at Managua on the Pacific Coast from the Troop Ship Henderson. There were two hundred fifty Marines held as reserves. What wasn't so funny at the start of the attack at Chinandega was four Marines were killed while sitting on the throne (royal seat) of their newly built head.

On January 29th the USS Richey was on patrol two miles seaward when one of the ship's spotters saw a large sailing craft close to the shore off Prinza Polka, "General Quarters." The ship's Captain, Lieutenant Commander Kling had two small boats lowered with five Marines in each with his Ensign and a Marine Sgt. They moved in on the sailing craft "smugglers" as they were unloading cases of rifles and ammunition. The Richey's Ensign and the sailing craft's crew with Marine guards sailed for port at Blue Fields. The four smugglers were turned over to Colonel Byrnes who said he would give them a fair trial. First he called for Sergeant Lukas to bring his small branding iron with the letter "M" on it. When the four smugglers saw the fire and the branding iron the Marines couldn't stop them from talking. When the interrogation was over Colonel Byrnes had each smuggler branded on the left cheek of his behind. He then had them dig holes for five graves for the Marine that were killed by sniper fire. Sergeant Lukas then tied the hands of each smuggler behind their back and he blindfolded them. The four smugglers were taken by horse and wagon to the Plaza Ciudad. They were put up against a wall and shot. They were left where they fell for two days with a sign as a warning. Colonel Byrnes said, "I hope the future generations deep-six the vicious killers who spy, sabotage, sexually kill, and discriminately cut up citizens in war and peace."

Major Pikus, Captain Wells, Lt. Sambach, and the two hundred fifty Marines were constantly being sniped at. They had lost eight men since they landed. Pikus said he was sending out Captain Wells with a party of sixty-five Marines. A search and destroy mission to work north of their camp. They would search out five miles along the coast and inland then form a half circle four miles out toward home base. Lt. Sambach's party after their five mile search would eventually meet up with Captain Wells' half circle after searching and destroying the insurgents and their campamento. Before Major Pikus left with his sixty-five Marines on their mission he checked out Gunnery Sgt. Itzkowitz's defense of their home base. Being satisfied Pikus then started out. All hell broke lose. They were attacked by a large party of insurgents. Gunnery Sgt. Itzkowitz's machine guns and 37mm field piece with canister shot killed the first rush of about fifty insurgents. Pikus and his one hundred and thirteen Marines charged the insurgents who broke and started to retreat. The Marines shot and bayoneted the insurgents without mercy. It was a slaughter. The insurgents who broke away would not come back to test the Marines again. Insurgent losses were one hundred twenty-five dead and twenty-five wounded who were shot. Marine losses were twenty-five dead and thirty wounded. Major Pikus left the twenty-five dead and thirty wounded with the thirty-three active Marines at home base. He took off with thirty Marines to go south and form the circle of search and destroy toward home base. Major Pikus' search and destroy mission added one hundred forty-five more insurgents dead. His total count with the attack was two hundred ninety-five and six campamento; demolish.

On February 4, 1912 Colonel Byrnes' scouts reported approximately four hundred insurgents with machine guns were headed toward Blue Fields. They were going to destroy the Constabulary and the Americano. They were now at Noarranca. Noarranco was a small farming aldea pueblo (village) in the hills. Colonel Byrnes had three hundred Marines, thirty corpsmen, two doctors, and twenty well armed sailors ready to travel. Two 37mm Field guns were added. Ammunition, water, rations, and medical supplies were on four wagons pulled by eight horses. A horse patrol of ten Marine guarded the wagons. Colonel Byrnes stopped his Marines one quarter of a mile outside of the village. He set up a perimeter waiting for his scout's reports on where the main force of insurgents was located. The insurgents sure of victory decided to attack. What a mistake on their part. Their leader El Principal with about one hundred fifty men attacked Byrnes' main body. The 37mm field guns with the canister shots plus machine guns annihilated El Principal who was killed leading his men. About one hundred of his men were killed in the first attack. The second attack did not help El Principal's second in command. About one hundred forty were killed. The Marine marksmen were having a field day. Byrnes ordered a frontal attack with bayonets. When it was over three hundred ten insurgents were killed and forty wounded. The wounded were shot. After the clean up Colonel Byrnes returned to the main base the Constabulary at Blue Fields. The Marines casualties were forty Marines killed twenty-seven wounded. El Principal did not know he was up against the best fighting force of Marines in the world.

On February 25, 1912 Colonel Byrnes, Major Pikus, and Major Kling were notified that the Officers and Marines from

A and B Companies were being replaced with Officers and Marines from their regiment Companies C and G. Company C from the USS Merrill troopship relieved Major Pikus and his Marines at Puerto Cabezas. Colonel Byrnes, Major Kling, and Lt. Eckert with their commands were relieved by G Company. Colonel Byrnes, Majors Kling and Pikus, Captains Wells and Zeke, and Lts. Sambach and Eckert were ordered to ILRP Headquarters at Washington, D.C. The three hundred and fifty-five Marines and sixty Navy men who survived the battles were ordered to Quantico, Virginia. After furloughs and decorations they would be trained as a Defensive Battalion. The IRLP Marines Colonel Byrnes, Majors Kling and Pikus, Captains Wells and Zeke, Lts. Sambach and Eckert made out their reports and were granted by Colonel Dell Rico a thirty day furlough. Before they left headquarter they were told problems were arising in Haiti and Santo Domingo. Majors Kling and Pikus couldn't wait to see their families. They took off after being dismissed. The Secretary of the Navy received a communication from the Troop Transport Henderson. - D- Company USMC was relieved and replaced February 28, 1912 at Managua, Nicaragua.

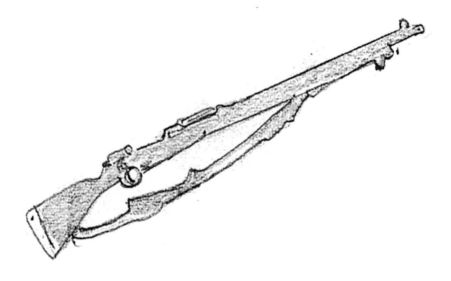

Chapter 13

Before we left for our furloughs we were told to report to our new location ILRP, Washington, D.C. on March 13, 1912. Colonel Dell Rico telephoned our Charge of Quarters Sergeant to tell the six of us; Majors Kling and Pikus, Captains Zeke and Wells, and Lieutenants Eckert and Sambach, be at the Commandant's meeting room at 1000 hours March 15th, dress uniforms. The Commandant and Colonel Dell Rico greeted us warmly as they always did. Coffee and small cakes were passed out. The Commandant said, "There is a problem in the Caribbean and our government wants us to intervene. We are still considered the protectorate of some islands in the Caribbean. There are two small islands off Port de Paix, Haiti. They are governed by Haiti. Voodoo is widely practiced on both islands. The latest reports are civil insurrection has started on both islands. The Haitian government said they can not control the local governments because of Voodooism a religion that some Haitian people believe in. One island named El Callaco is about one mile in length by two and a quarter miles wide. I would like Major Kling, Captain Zeke, and Lt. Eckert to check this island out. Your instructions are to "deep six" the insurgents bandits. It is believed because of this Voodoo you are going to have a lot of trouble. These people kill for their religion. Be careful who you trust or you may end up a dead chicken. You people know what kind of arms and equipment you will need. Do not leave yourself short on anything. See the Quarter Master at Quantico, Va. Major Pikus, Captain Wells, and Lt. Sambach you people heard what instructions I gave to Major Kling and his unit. The same applies to you people. The name of the island you have to clean out is Rio San Negro. It is about one mile and three quarters in length and one mile wide. Word just came in that on El Callaco the Voodoo leader is El Baspito Trujillo. He has about two hundred Voodooist people with him. The population of the island is about three hundred fifty. Farming, fishing, bananas, coconuts, trading, hat weaving, and yams are the main industries. Major Kling the only names we have on the insurgent banditos are Juan Pebas and El Pedro Gamboa now on the island of Rio San Negro. This island's industry is the same as El Callaco. These bandits are believed to have two machine guns, small arms, and enough ammunition for a small war. It is also believed you will run into some foreign interventionists. You know what to do with them. Don't forget hand grenades and branding irons. Ha, ha, ha! I will say I approve of your method of interrogation. Lieutenant Commander Kling, Captain of the USS Richey knows the coastline off these islands. He will leave each unit off at a prearranged spot. A location he has logged. You have two days only to complete the mission. Major Pikus' unit will leave the Destroyer Richey at 0200 hours and Major Kling's unit at 2400 hours. You people will be picked up on the second night at the prearranged spots. Same time and location of your departure."

A small row boat was put over the side of the Richey for Kling's unit. The destroyer was a quarter of a mile off the shore of Timor, El Callaco. Rowing was no problem. Zeke rowed. All the way in they heard drums beating first loudly then softly. They hid the boat in the jungle shore line then walked inland about two hundred yards and saw a clearing with a fifty foot half circle. Tied to a post was a dark skinned woman with her hands behind her back. She was half naked. Sitting by a small fire two half naked men were looking at each other as if in a trance. Kling's unit moved slowly along the ground behind the two men. They put their loops of wire, thugger style around their throats, and garroted their knives to finish the job. They threw their bodies about twenty-five feet back in the jungle. The unit proceeded to the outskirts of Timor with the woman they had freed. The woman said she knew this area. She showed them where some of the Voodoo big shots lived, where they had guns, ammunition, and food stored, also, their boats and the motor boats that they used to go off shore to commit piracy. She said she had been kidnapped from the Village of Chaco about three miles south of Timor.

107

Every once in a while they needed a woman who they thought might be a virgin to sacrifice to their Voodoo God. She said the Voodoo goofs paraded her around the town of Timor for two days. She saw where they kept their guns and supplies and she believed they would rape her then sacrifice her. She knew they cut people up. Their priest or chief would do the job. She heard they would cut off the woman's tits and cut out her sexual areas, drain her blood, and drink it. "Nice guys, and we Marines should let these people live. Deep six them all!" Kling took his unit further in the jungle to make plans.

On board the Richey while going to their destinations two Haitian political refugees checked their speech and apparel. The units needed more makeup to darken their hands, necks, and faces. Major Pikus and his unit were landed just off the shore in a small boat about one quarter of a mile from Rio San Negro. They ran up the beach into the jungle. It was a good thing they ran up fast because guards were patrolling the beach. They walked and came to a path just as it was becoming daylight. An elderly man was hardly making it on his own. Pikus stepped in to help him. He said, "Americano, Lord has answered my prayer." His English was understandable. He said a pig by the name of El Baptisto Trujillo and Migell Rosa Piabio called the Chacalo Adive (jackal) made him a cripple by torturing him because he would not participate in Voodooism. "There is a house," he said, "by the crossroads to Rio San Negro, a large house where the Voodoo people and their chiefs meet. They keep their guns, ammunition, food, and dynamite in two rooms always guarded by armed men. They look like they are in a trance. Real weird! They are having a big sacrifice tomorrow night. They usually start when it gets dark." He said if we were going to do any damage to Migell and Trujillo he would like to help. Pikus asked if they had any motor boats. The man said they had two new motor boats tied up about a quarter of a mile down the road from the house at a small dock. Pikus said to his unit, "If they are all together we may be able to finish this job in one night. We may have to use their boats to get off the island. We would be better off waiting for the Richey out on the prearranged sea area. I don't think we will be able to fight off what will be left of them. This is a small island to hide on."

Major Kling and his unit also thought about getting off Timor, El Callaco by boat, but then what would they do? Eckert would go down to the boats, keep the two motor boats and run their motors. He would be ready to take off and make sure they had extra cans of gasoline.

When Eckert got down to where the boats were docked he saw two guards both with rifles. He went off in the bush and whistled out loud. One of the guards walked down to see who had whistled. Eckert garroted him, knifed him, and then pulled him further down in the bush. He then crept behind the other guard and knifed him. He checked out the two motor boats and started sinking the other boats. Kling and Zeke told the woman they had saved to go down to the dock and hide out until they came for her. She would probably see Eckert. They then walked up to the house the woman had told them had guns and supplies. About a hundred people were walking in and out of the house. It was dark. The Voodoo people had a few lanterns for light and a big fire was going outside the house. A female person they believed to be dead was tied to a post. A pool of blood was at her feet. They walked into the house and saw where the guarded rooms were located. On the way out they saw six men drinking and talking in another room. From outside they located the windows of the rooms not guarded. The windows of the rooms with the supplies had screens and were open. They cut the screens with their knives. Kling and Zeke each had two hand grenades. They tied two together. They both had a window and on the count they pulled the pins, threw the grenades into the rooms, and then took off. They were on the other side of the hill and were protected when the explosion occurred. The house was gone. Many people were dead or wounded. Kling and Zeke saw who they believed were the leaders of the Voodoo gang, Juan Pebas and El Pedro Gamboa and many of their dead men. A couple of live worshippers identified their leaders. The next

109

day Kling and Zeke had no opposition. They walked down to the docks. They saw the Richey off shore. A large whale boat was coming into the dock with about twenty-five Haitian Troops from Haiti. With them was one of the Haitian political refugees from the Richey. The woman went with the political leader. Kling, Zeke, and Eckert were picked up by the Richey. Their job was finished.

Pikus and his unit helped the older Haitian up to about one hundred yards away from the house. The old Haitian said, "Let's get closer." Five men with rifles walked past their hiding place. With the help of the moon light the old Haitian identified Trutillo and Migell. Pikus told the old Haitian to try to make his way to the dock. Wells and Sambach had their rifles ready. Two men walked out on the porch. Pikus was ready with two revolvers. The lanterns on the porch helped to identify Migell and Trutillo. Wells and Sambach shot both of them. Four men came out of the front door. The two revolvers of Pikus' joined in with the rifle fire of Wells and Sambach. All the men were killed. Pikus tied the grenades around the dynamite with light wire they found. The wire went inside the grenade loops, the pins were loosely tied with a knot, and carefully they ran the wire outside the house as far as they considered safe, and then pulled the wire. The explosion had the desired results. When the USS Richey's Captain Kling heard the explosion he had no doubt the three Marines would not be waiting at the deep water dock at Rio San Negro. Pikus gave the old Haitian all the money they had. The USS Richey picked up the unit. The Haitian Troops now hearing and seeing what six Marines did about Voodoo moved into the two islands. The USS Richey sailed for Norfolk, Virginia. No casualties. A job well done for the Haitian Government.

Chapter 14

Borfirio Diaz, President of the Mexican government was alleged to be overthrown in 1910 - 1911. Serious problems developed. The Federalist and Revolutionary parties started to take over. "It appears one worse than the other." On June 6, 1912 our president said we have to protect American property. The Revolutionary parties said they were going to take land away from the large estate owners and give land to the Mexican peasants. A man now in office called President Carptanzel said bandits were trying to seize the government. Banditry broke out in Sonora, Chihuahua, Durango, Coahuila, Nuevo, and the Guerrero areas of Mexico. Some American business men were killed and all Americans who had any interest in oil, gold, or real estate were at peril. The Revolutionary parties said Diaz had no right originally to let foreigners take over Mexican oil wells and mines. The State Department, War Department, and the Navy Department USA asked the Marine Commandant Smith if his I.R.O.S. teams were still active. The Departments wanted people they could trust to: 1) get information on the two parties trying to run the government of Mexico, 2) protect American lives and interests, 3) "Deep six" all bandits that have killed American citizens, 4) look for corruption and Americans selling guns and ammunition, 5) intervention by other governments, and 6) burn all people somniterum and cannabis sativa marijuana plants.

Colonel Dell Rico telephoned the Headquarters and asked Majors Kling and Pikus, Captains Zeke and Wells, and Lts. Eckert and Sambach if they were interested in this assignment. They all volunteered. They were told if apprehended by any parties or bandits in Mexico they were working on their own. They were also bandits. Colonel Dell Rico told the six Officers to be ready to leave their Headquarters at 1100 hours. Transportation had been arranged to take them to Quantico, Virginia. The former I.R.O.S. Headquarters building would be their home for twenty days. A Mexican Captain by the name of Juan G. Sandoual a Linguist teacher of Mexican languages and dialects would be with them for seven days. Mayan Mexican dialects and Spanish language shall be the daily language. They will fire the single action and new Frontier Army Colt Revolvers, 44 spec., and 45 caliber (5 1/2 and 7 1/2 barrels). The Model 94 lever action 30-30 Winchester and Model 94XTR will also be fired. Equipment, ammunition, rations, and money will be issued. Probably the same equipment issued as the Indian assignment. "You people will let you hair and mustache grow and start walking and looking the part you are about to play. Take showers once in a while. Ha, ha, ha!" "Major Pikus' and Captain Wells' areas are Sonora, Chihuahua, Coahuila, and Nuevo. Major Kling's and Captain Zeke's areas are Durango, Zacatecas, Michoacán, Mexico City, and Guerrero. Lts. Eckert's and Sanbach's areas are Oaxaca, Chiapas, Campeche, and Yucatan. Colonel Byrnes' headquarters will be El Paso, Texas, Captain Conrad's headquarters Laredo, Texas. All information to Colonel Byrnes and Captain Conrad. Contacts will pick up Lts. Eckert and Sambach from the Destroyer Richey about two miles out in the Gulf of Mexico also, Majors Kling and Zeke off of Paxpan. Arrangements will be made for pickup. Major Pikus and Captain Wells will leave from El Paso. Take nothing with you that can identify you as Americans. Horses and equipment will be purchased or stolen in Mexico. Remember "Kill or be Killed."

Major Pikus and Captain Wells were able to get over the border without any trouble at Ciudad Juarez. They purchased two horses, saddles, and other equipment. They made sure no American Manufacturing labels were on the purchases. They rode to Nacomaride Garcia a small village that was having one big problem. About one hundred fifty Federal Troops were going to have a public hanging; they were going to hang the Mayor, his helpers, and two women because they were Revolutionists. On the outskirts of the town two hundred Revolutionists were getting ready to attack. Pikus saw that their leadership was bad. A frontal attack would wipe them out. He approached the leader and identified himself as a Revolutionist Army Officer. Pikus said he could lead his men with a minimum of casualties. The leader agreed. He did not have any experience on attacking trained troops. Pikus never did like the Federal Mexican Troops. They were always killing more peasants than they had to. The hangings were set for 0900 hours the next morning. Pikus told the Revolutionist leader to put fifteen men on each entrance and exit of the village. That would be thirty men. No Federal Troops were going to escape. The Federal Troops were all quartered together on the right side of the village square and their horses on the left side. Pikus told the leader, "Place fifty men on the left flank and fifty on the right flank with twenty-five men in the prone position and twenty-five men in the kneeling position. All this is to be done quietly. At first light when the Federal Troops are in formation at the signal, command firing, then fire at will. Ten of your men will be ready to lead the horses away. Fifteen men will back up the machine gun the Federals have set up." Pikus and Wells would take the machine gun with three men and crawl up in the early dark hours of the morning. Ten men would be ready to run in and free the people to be hung. At 0630 hours it was almost day light and the Federal Troops were lined up for the inspection before breakfast. It was a slaughter! The Revolutionist Leader called Pikus and Wells "El Conquer" (conquerors). The casualties of the Revolutionists was ten dead and twenty-five wounded. Pikus' and Wells' fame would be spread. They were given a metal tag for identification. Forty-five Federal Troopers tried to surrender; they were all killed including the thirty wounded. One leader and twenty-five Revolutionists asked Pikus if they could escort him. Pikus said to Wells, "Why not? We can use the help." Pikus' and Wells' next stop was Chihuahua. With the help of his escorts Pikus was introduced to the principal leader who controlled the Revolutionary activities in the four areas that Pikus was to investigate. His name was General Carlora Rios. He told Pikus he wanted a United Mexican country and help from the United States on coal, gas, silver, gold, and oil problems. Mexico did not have the qualified help. He said that Mexico has communication, food, and health problems and that the U.S. has the knowledge to solve most of these problems. General Rios gave Pikus three other names: Generals Federico Perez, Eduardo Leardo, and Juan Estrada. General Rios told Pikus he had just come from Mexico City, the Capital and that he had information for the U.S. State and War Departments. Pikus said he would get the information out without delay. Pikus contacted Colonel Byrnes who contacted the State Department in Washington, D.C. General Rios said Villa and Zapata were supposed to be Revolutionists and they were also bandits. The new government would take care of them. Pikus and Wells stayed at General Rios' headquarters and received the following message from Colonel Byrnes: Present assignments are cancelled. All units contact Colonel Byrnes for pickup to home base.

LIEUTENANT COMMANDER
FRANK EKLING
USN

Chapter 15

After the Mexican assignment the seven ILRP Officers returned to their headquarters at Washington, D.C. It was June 27, 1912. The Duty Sergeant told Colonel Byrnes he had a telephone call from Colonel Dell Rico. Byrnes was to telephone Colonel Dell Rico as soon as he reported in. Byrnes said, "O happy day!" He then telephoned Dell Rico's office. Dell Rico was not in his office. His secretary told Colonel Byrnes to arrange a meeting at ILRP Headquarters June 30 at 0900 hours. A two day leave was granted for the unit.

June 30, 1912 was a hot day. The fans in the ILRP meeting room did not help. The meeting room was small and only had two windows. Colonel Dell Rico was fifteen minutes late and blamed it on traffic. His warmly greeting. "It's about time you people had a Caribbean vacation again. Any volunteers? Thank you Marines. You know if the Army and the Navy ever look at the Caribbean scenes they will find the islands guarded by United States Marines. "Rum and Aqua seltzer soda." Now the problem! Trouble has flared up again in Nicaragua. The insurgents supported by the banditos are over running the areas of Masaya and Coyo Tepe. There are not enough Marines at our Constabulary at Blue Fields to take care of the uprisings. The War Department gave the problem to Commandant Smith. The Commandant said he wants a free hand. He will consult his ILRP Officers. They have fought there and know the areas. You people know the score. How many volunteers? 100%, you people live a charmed life. Orders for the campaign and procedures are almost completed. Colonel Byrnes, Majors Pikus and Kling will report to Commandant Smith's office July 1 at 0930 hours."

After Colonel Dell Rico left the ILRP Office Colonel Byrnes said he had to look over his mail. One letter looked like it had traveled all over the southern States.

From: Warrant Officer Louie Byrnes
                    Naval Gun Repairs
                    Norfolk, Virginia

To: Colonel E Byrnes
        Installation and Logistics
        545 Independence Road
        Washington, D.C.

Dear Colonel Byrnes,

I left the USS Harry Lee nine months ago and decided on some naval Schooling. I completed the Naval requirements and was promoted to Warrant Officer W-3. My training program was Destroyer Command, Destroyer Construction, Gun Control, Repair and Shell I.D. I now have sixteen years in the Navy and qualified as a Gunnery Officer. The DD Richey 385 is in Dry dock for repairs. I hope to get a berth on it. It was told they needed a Gunnery Officer.

Say hello to the rest of the unit.

                              Your cousin,
                              Louie

Byrnes said to himself, "Good luck Louie."

We had to wait one half hour to see the Commandant. Colonel Dell Rico asked how the training programs were going. The Commandant walked in and said, "Good morning Marines." He said, "We have the Caribbean problem again. I am sending three Battalions to Nicaragua. We thought the Nicaraguan government had the country under control. Major Kling will be in command of Battalion C."

Battalion -C-
Five hundred fifty personnel
Two companies

Company A – Captain Zeke

1st Platoon – Lt. Tom Lefty Miller – 80 Riflemen
2nd Platoon – Lt. Tom Cook – 80 Heavy Weapons
    Lt. Louie Jones – 37mm and 75mm packs
3rd Platoon – Lt. Foster - 10 Communicators
    12 Headquarters – 14 Cooks
    10 – Security Guards – 10 Transportation

4th Platoon –Lt. Carl Blake – 11 Riflemen – 12 Engineers
12 Ammunition and Rations
Landing area Puerto Cabezas

Medical
2 Navy Doctors
2 Chaplains
20 Navy Corpsmen
Off the coast near Corn is the Hospital Ship Nightingale

Battalion - B-
Major R Pikus – Commander
Companies G & I
Captain L. Wells
Lt. Ron Smith – 1st Platoon
Lt. Liverex – 2nd Platoon
Lt. Peters – 3rd Platoon
Lt. Tom Walt – 4th Platoon
Lt. Joseph Wilson – Reserve
275 personnel
275 held in reserve
The same T.O. of personnel and weapons as Company -A-
Landing area San Juan Del Norte

Battalion -A-
Colonel Walter Quick
Major Harry Bean
Same T.O. as Battalion C & B
Pacific Ocean Side
From San Diego, California

Company -C- 275 personnel to land at Managua and move south to Masaya where some of the trouble is. 275 Marines and Navy personnel to land at Chinandega and work southeast. The Maryland, three Destroyers as escorts, and one Destroyer APB will be used as a Hospital ship. One transport ship with supplies will stand by off

Managua, Nicaragua.

Command Post: Major R. Byrnes, Blue Fields
Communications I.D. ILRP M-7
Lt. Eckert and Lt. Sambach I.D. Officers

Battalion -A- Company E to work eastward. Battleship
Maryland with 200 Marines in reserve. Battleship North
Carolina off the East coast of Prinzapolca, Nicaragua. 200
Marines and 200 Marines in reserve.

D-L- Day July 18, 1912 0830 hours what a day for landing.
Big rain storm over most of Nicaragua all the troops landed as
scheduled. Company -C- from Battalion -A- had one hell of a
fight at Masaya. It was good planning that Company -F- was
close by to help. The battle lasted three days. The Marines
fixed bayonets and finished the job. Insurgents and banditos
casualties were four hundred and twenty dead, fifty captured
and the wounded were shot. Marine casualties Company -
C- fifty Marines dead, twenty-seven wounded. Company -
F- twenty-five dead and thirty-seven wounded. Battalion -A-
with four hundred and eleven Marines and Navy personnel
were told to stay in the area until relieved.

Battalion -C- Major Kling and Captain Zeke were on their
second landing at Puerto Cabezas. No opposition to this
landing. They moved company -A- inland a half mile from
the sea water. They used this location before, a clear area with
a small stream. After posting security, machine guns, 37mm
grenade traps, and wire Captain Zeke called all Platoon
Leaders to his tent. He told them to be careful of their health
habits. "Check your platoons frequently on drinking water,
food, dysentery, clean lines, and mosquitoes. Tell the Marines
to use their nets. Be very careful on guard duty. This enemy
creeps up on you very quietly. Two Marines on each post.
Don't Fall Asleep Or You Are A Dead Marine. Don't Smoke
On Guard Duty, You give Your Location To The Enemy. Don't
have Anything On Your Person That Smells Or Makes A

118

<u>Noise.</u> Now, you Platoon Leaders get your Marines together and pass the word.

Major Kling's control tent was on the portside, Captain Zeke's starboard side. All Marines from the General down are riflemen. Marines daily pleasure; mud, rain, sand, fleas, mosquitoes, heat, and being sniped at.

July 20, 1912 Captain Zeke again checked his company security. The area was not too large. He made sure the machine guns, 37mm, and mortars were well placed with avenues of fire that were clear. Weapons were cleaned and not too oily. All supplies, ammo, and grenades were issued. After evening chow the Marines returned to their tent areas. Just before twilight the entertainment started. Snipers from all angles were shooting in the camp. How did these people get so close without our scouts reporting? Post number one was over run by about twenty-five armed horsemen. The Marine machine gunners on Post one quickly recovered and stopped the horsemen with lighted torches and others who were trying to enter the camp. The Marines fixed bayonets and started shooting. The armed horsemen who got into the camp killed ten Marines and wounded twelve. Major Kling shot two of the horsemen. In all sixty armed horsemen and twenty running insurgents and banditos were killed. One of the Nikko Scouts who was not dead said they killed the five Marine Scouts and sold the Marines out to the insurgents and banditos. Major Kling telegraphed the USS Richey to send a boat in and pick up the wounded. The camp settled down and got ready for a search and destroy mission.

The USS Richey was back on Station Coastal Security on July 15. Louie was Gunnery Officer. Before sailing Lieutenant Commander Kling had a long talk with Louie on discipline on his ship. He did not have to tell Louie anything about discipline and gunnery. Louie was one tough son- of-a- bitch the Navy had at this time. He was fair and trained his sailors on every weapon on the ship including the 03 rifle and .45 caliber pistol. He had been called "One shot Louie" at one time; it was still true. His gun crews loved him and were

119

one of the best gun crews in the Navy. Twelve PFCs, two Corporals, and one Gunnery Sergeant were stationed on the Richey for boarding and landings. They all knew of Louie's fighting with the Marines in Nicaragua. Everyone respected Louie.

Major Kling was not happy about the thirty Marine casualties. His command now had two hundred forty-five Marines and Navy men. Two hundred twenty-one fighting Marines. He called for Captain Zeke and all Platoon leaders to meet in the mess tent. He said he was going to leave twenty rifle Marines and twelve heavy weapons Marines at the camp, two machine guns, one 37mm, and two mortars, also ten Marines for other duties, cooks, etc. Lt. Carl Blake would be in command. Captain Zeke with eighty-nine Marines, riflemen, and heavy weapons on pack mules will travel south three miles from the coast towards Coyo Tepe. Colonel Byrnes was at center control at the Blue Fields Constabulary. He had two hundred Marines in reserve. With eighty-nine Marines I am going to travel west for six miles toward Ocotal then turn south. I should be within three miles of Coyo Tepe. I will send out my scouts and wait to hear from Major Pikus and his company. Captain Zeke's column will turn west at Piri to meet us. I intend after the scout's reports to use the 75 packs and mortars then cover the right flank leaving Zeke to cover the frontal area. Major Pikus up from the south will cover the rear and left flank driving the insurgents and bandits toward the Atlantic Ocean. Three destroyers are stationed to pick off any of these bastards who try to escape. Major Pikus traveling north destroyed three small villages killing twenty-seven bandits. He lost six Marines to snipers and four on the search and destroy mission. His scouts made contact with Kling's and Zeke's scouts.

It was now August 1st, 1912. On August 4th the action was scheduled to start at Coyo Tepe. All scouts reported. The estimations of scouts added up to five hundred insurgents and bandits, six machine guns, and two small cannons. Their outer defenses had about one hundred fifty snipers in trees, holes, and trenches. Major Kling sent his scouts out to tell Zeke, Pikus, and Wells to each send out twenty-five Marines quietly in the dark and spread them out about five hundred yards from Coyo Tepe. At daylight kill as many snipers as they can with rifle fire and grenades. Before daylight Pikus, Zeke, and Wells should have their machine guns and 37mm guns on high ground to cover all angles. At 0630 hours the pack 75mms will shell the town for approximately twenty minutes. Machine gun fire and canister shot from the 37mms should cut enough of them down. Every Marine who can use a rifle with a bayonet will take over the town. Nicaraguan Constabulary Police will shortly take over what's left of the town.

After what the Marines saw two days before on the trail four males with their heads and private parts cut off and body gutted made the Marines ferocious. Approximately three hundred Marines with rifles, bayonets, grenades, machine guns, and four 37mms shooting canister shot at trees, bushes, houses insurgents, and bandits made Marine history. Most of these Marines had been down this vacation spot of the Caribbean before and they wanted to end it for awhile. The fight in the bush with snipers and in the town was one the old timers in the Marines would never forget. The Marines shot, bayoneted, rifle butted, clubbed, and knifed the bandit insurgents. Marines also died. Majors Kling and Pikus were in the middle of the fight where they should not have been. They had their hands full. Kling with cuts on his arms and legs was also shot in the fleshy part of his left foot. He was back with Pikus who was cut in the legs and chest shooting and bayoneting with 03 rifles. Wells and Zeke rescued them back to a command location. After five hours of fighting the Marines were victorious. There were sixteen hundred and fifty Marines and Navy personnel available for the campaign; two uprisings, search and destroy, snipering, and medical problems. Nine hundred Marines and one hundred Navy Medical Corpsmen participated in the actual fighting. Three hundred eighty-four casualties for the Marines and Navy. Two hundred dead, one hundred eighty-four wounded. The Coyo Tepe casualties already were included in the total; ninety-one Marines killed and seventy-seven wounded.

The Nicaraguan troops trained at Blue Fields and Matagalpa by US Marines took over the towns of Coyo Tepe and Masaya. Majors Kling and Pikus with the wounded Marines and Navy Corpsmen were transferred to the hospital ship Nightingale, then to the hospital at Quantico, Va. Captains Wells and Zeke went back to Puerto Cabezas with seventy-five Marines to set up a Constabulary with the forty-two Marines Kling left with Lt. Carl Blake. After the Constabulary was set up Lt. Carl Blake would be in command. The USS Richey would bring in supplies, and then take Captains Wells and Zeke to their home port at Norfolk, Va. Wells and Zeke will return to the ILRP Headquarters. Colonel Byrnes will also be picked up by the Richey then take the train from Norfolk to Washington, D.C. where he will report to Colonel Dell Rico. Colonel Walter Quick will leave eighty men and supplies to set up a Constabulary at Masaya with the Nicaraguan troops trained by the Marines. He will leave Major Henry Bean in command. His wounded should be on the Hospital Destroyer APD. The rest of his command will leave on the transport and Battleship Maryland for San Diego. A job well done by Colonel Walter Quick and his Marines. Grave registration units from Quantico were on their way to Nicaragua. Lts. Eckert's and Sambach's orders were to remain at Blue Fields and train Nicaraguan soldiers at the Constabulary.

Chapter 16

On October, 1912 Majors Kling and Pikus were discharged from the hospital at Quantico, Va. Their wounds were not bad enough for a medical discharge; anyway the Commandant would not release them from service. He gave them a one month recovery leave. Something new! He told Colonel Dell Rico he wanted Colonel Byrnes, Majors Kling and Pikus, Captains Zeke and Wells, and Lieutenants Eckert and Sambach at the ILRP Headquarters for a meeting at 0930 hours December 20, 1912. When Majors Pikus' and Kling's leaves are up they will report to ILRP Headquarters. Pikus's and Kling's wives were happy to have their husbands home for a change. They each had two small children. The children asked their mothers how long the two men were going to stay. The wives told the children they are your daddies. Pikus' little son said, "Now we see them, then they are gone. What kind of work do Marines do that keeps their daddies away?" When their wives were off duty from the hospital they took their families on a tour around Washington, the museums, and the Jefferson Memorial, some house parties, playing with the children, fixing up this and that, and then the recovery leave was over. Kling and Pikus reported to the Medical Officer at Quantico Hospital on December 2nd, 1912 where they received a clean bill of health. Fit for duty! The ILRP Headquarters Duty Sergeant told them Wells, Zeke, Sambach, and Eckert would be there by December 14th. Pikus and Kling could go home nights from the ILRP Headquarters.

On December 14th they heard the USS Richey was in port at Norfolk, Va. Kling got off a telegram to his brother on the Richey inviting him to his home over the holidays. Colonel Byrnes invited Louie to his home for the holidays. Lieutenant Commander Kling and Louie were glad to receive the invitations. They all met at the ILRP Headquarters on December 16th. Kling's kids thought they had another daddy when they met his brother. Wells, Zeke, Eckert, and Sambach had sleeping quarters at ILRP. Every other night the nine Officers had a party at different houses. They played cards, sang, and played with the children. All clean fun! The Commandant of the Marine Corps notified Colonel Byrnes that he had permission from the Navy Department to hold Lieutenant Commander Kling and Warrant Officer Byrnes for the meeting on December 20th, also if both Officers fitted in the new assignment the Commander Ship Richey could be available. When the officers of ILRP, Lt. Commander Kling, and Warrant Officer Byrnes heard this they decided to have a one night card playing poker game and get drunk. They were all very happy. December 20, 1912 was a cold day. Colonel Dell Rico was ten minutes late for the meeting. The Commandant was twenty-five minutes late. So, what else is new for meeting time? After greeting Commandant Smith said, "We have one little problem that I am sure you nine Officers can correct. In your favorite vacation areas we have a problem. We have piracy in the Caribbean and South Atlantic Ocean areas. On the Atlantic Ocean side we have two islands where the pirates are alleged to have their headquarters on Mona and Pinnero Islands. These two islands are northeast of Puerto Rico. The information I have from the Navy Department stated Warrant Officer Louie Byrnes knows these islands better than he knows his own name. First of all, who volunteers for this job? All hands say 100%. Do you people ever say no? Now that I have your attention I would like to hear from Warrant Officer Byrnes." Before Louie could speak an aide came into the room and handed the Commandant a paper. The Commandant smiled and said, "Effective December 18th 1912 Warrant Officer Louie Byrnes was promoted to Lieutenant J.G. The report reads on after looking over his record, experience, and latest fitness report the Naval Service needs men of his background as Officers. Citations, record changes, and warrant shall be mailed to the Officer, re: USS Richey #385 Norfolk, Va." This was Louie's greatest moment. Congratulations from the Commandant of the Marine Corps, his ship's Commander Lt. Commander Kling, and the nine Officers of the ILRP Unit of the Marine Corps. "Now Louie," the Commandant said, "I am going to make you earn your one half inch with one quarter inch stripe! Tell us what you know about these islands. Let's take Mona then Pinnero." Louie said both of these islands are occupied. Count Mona out, a few fishermen, no water. "Now, sir you said a little problem! I heard a couple of pleasure boats belonging to the rich have been boarded, probably some Senator's or Congressman's. This has been going on for years and not always reported. A lot of these big executives take their girlfriends on a boat ride for a week or weekend. They tell their wives they have to go to the Caribbean Islands on business. I believe I know who is in back of this piracy. I think it comes from Pinnero Island. Dirty Neck Harry and Phil the Jib have been getting away with this for years. They have two small steam power boats with sails, both very sea worthy. Some of the bad island boys are always looking to make a dollar and help by looking for small pleasure boats. Seasonal work for them. Dirty Neck and the Jib sail their boats out on the water and wait for small boats that pass the island and look like they may have something of value aboard. They get close and signal that their boat is in distress. When the boats get close out comes the guns, they tie up to the boat they are robbing, then they take off. They take everything that is not nailed down. I have never heard of them doing damage to the people or the boats they rob. I think we can nip these two bastards and solve the present problem. We can fix them and their boats. When the islands hear what happens to them you can forget about piracy for awhile. If the Richey drops me and one Officer of the ILRP unit off at night about 2300 hours in an old sailboat we can get to the dock. These guys know me. I will tell them the Navy threw me out for stealing. This guy I am with is a thief wanted by the Puerto Rican Police – no reward. We should carry old type revolvers and knives, nothing new. We also should have some jewelry we "stole" so we can barter for food and drink. A couple of gold coins. Most of the bad guys as well as some good island people deal at Brucie's Trade Market Bar and Grill. His girlfriend Big Hattie runs the show.

125

Brucie deals with everything that is not nailed down. He sits around smoking cigars all day. He has a couple of his own kids running around learning the trade. Dirty Neck and the Jib live in a five room house. They visit Brucie's Bar every night. They each have three or four girls with them. They eat and drink the best they can steal. Now if the Richey can drop off the other four ILRP Officers the next night not too far from the dock we will have enough help to grab Dirty Neck and the Jib and take them out in the bush. Believe me when we get finished with them piracy should stop. No killing. No blood if we can help. We will put a sign on them. A Marine specialty. The double M on both cheeks and a small M on their ding-a-lings. The Richey should be at the dock by 0200 hours. We will blow up their boats and the dock."

The problem was completed as planned on January 15th 1913.

Louie

Chapter 17

February 15, 1913 Communication - #1506 from Admiral W.C. Scott Navy Number 1-A-RA-USN, Navy Department, Washington, D.C. to Admiral J. Jones South Atlantic, Caribbean Area Command Guantanamo Bay. Subject: Promotion Lieutenant Commander Frank E. Kling - Richey 385 Navy No. 401662 USN Your Command - to- Commander effective February 14, 1913 Commander F. Kling will take command of Flotilla Unit 1, South Atlantic, Caribbean Sea areas. Destroyers Jones 386, Smith 387, James 388, Able 389, and Louis 390, are assigned. The Richey 385 shall be Flotilla Command Headquarters. Communicate to: General Smith Commandant United States Marine Corps Washington, D.C. Colonel Byrnes ILRP, Installations and Logistics Headquarters 545 Independence Road Washington, D.C.

Gunner Louie was now a full Lieutenant and in charge of gunnery on the USS Richey. He was promoted to Inspector on all weapons of Unit One Destroyers. The Navy Department wanted to transfer Louie to other units. Louie said, "If you transfer me I will retire." He wanted to stay on the Richey. That was his home. Home ports for Flotilla Unit -1- are Key West Naval Station, San Juan, Puerto Rico, Navy Yard Norfolk, Virginia, and Guantanamo Bay, Cuba.

February 20, 1913 ILRP Officers Colonel L. Byrnes, Majors Kling and Pikus, Captains Zeke and Wells, Lts. Sambach and Eckert were ordered to report for Medical Fitness Examinations on or before February 25, 1913. Everyone passed. Majors Pikus and Kling now were in the Marines for eleven years. Kling was twenty-nine years of age and Pikus was thirty-one. Home life, furloughs, going home nights from ILRP Headquarters was great. Pikus' and Kling's children were growing up and they now knew their fathers. Life was great! All good things came to and end. Major Kling was ordered to Quantico, Va. Marine Base. His orders were to take Battalion -"B"- on landings and training exercises on Crab Island, South Shore in the Caribbean. General Smith gave him some special orders before he left Washington. Three hundred enlisted Marines were in the Battalion as well as his Executive Officer Captain Zeke, his training Officer Lt. Eckert, two Navy Doctors, and twenty Navy Corpsmen, and personnel, his Troopship the Henderson, and Escort Destroyers the James 388 and Able 389. The Destroyers were only to stay for two days shelling on landing exercises then report back to their assigned duty. Major Pikus had the same maneuver plans for Battalion -"C"-. His transport was the Pearson, Escorts, Gunboats Monroe and Doctrine for shore shelling. His Battalion was to land on the Atlantic Ocean side, North Shore of Crab Island. His Executive Officer Captain Wells, his Training Officer Lt. Sambach. Pikus had the same number of Navy personnel, two doctors and 20 corpsmen.

Training exercises were to go on for three months. The two Battalions departed Norfolk, Va. March 25, 1913. They were to return June 10, 1913. Besides landing, intense training on bayonet, knife, hand to hand combat, field sanitation, first aid, and field problems. Also, they would receive intense training on the 1903 Springfield rifle, the new Browning machine gun, and .45 cal. pistol. Everyone must qualify.

Commander Kling's ship the Richey was patrolling southeast from Puerto Rico in the Caribbean off the islands of St. Thomas and St. John. The lookout of the Richey reported a ship he believed was a destroyer traveling south in the ocean lane the Richey was traveling. The destroyer was headed right for the Richey. Kling signaled and used the code for identification. No response. Kling told Louie to shoot two three inchers, both shots at midships, port, and starboard side. Boy! Did that destroyer move. It identified itself as the German Destroyer Von Housen. Kling told their captain to stand by. His signalman repeated. The Von Housen's Captain said he was having problems with his ship. Kling telegraphed Guantanamo Bay Naval Command. He was told to let the Von Housen proceed. A Diplomatic Situation. Someone in Washington forgot to notify the Caribbean Command at Guantanamo Bay Naval. The German ship was lucky. Louie's gun crew would have "deep sixed" it in fifteen minutes.

The Navy was lucky to have Commander Kling, his Flotilla, and Louie in the Caribbean areas. They wouldn't let a fly get by. The gun runners, pirates, foreign interventions, dope and opium peddlers were very fearful of Kling's Flotilla. No mercy was shown. One shot Louie and his crew never missed. The Richey just had enough water to dock at Isabella Secunda's dock on Crab Island. The Gunboat Monroe was at the dock. Their Captain Sandy Cross was asked to be at Commander Kling's wardroom aboard the Richey at 1500 hours April 7, 1913. Majors Pikus and Kling were also asked to be aboard. When all were aboard including Lt. Louie Commander Kling opened his special orders. Captain Cross, his gun boat and crew were to take Major Pikus, Kling, and Lt. Louie Byrnes to Pinero Island to check out Brucie's Bar and Trading Co. They were also to look over Dirty Neck Harry and The Jib. It appears some interventionists were visiting many islands. When Pikus, Kling, and Louie entered Brucie's Bar Dirty Neck and The Jib started to run out. Pikus called them back and told them to sit down. Brucie's love life Big Hattie, Dirty Neck, and The Jib were interrogated separately. The only one who knew what they were looking for was Brucie. Dirty Neck and The Jib were playing it straight. No problems. They were working for Brucie. Brucie told them that a Spanish fellow by the name of Juan Siena had a night club and trading co. outside the town of Ciebo just off the coast of Ensenada Honda, Puerto Rico. Brucie believed Siena had dealings with the insurgents, interventionist, coke dealers, and people who were stealing for a living. Siena and his thieves had a field day robbing U.S. Military personnel who visited his bar and whorehouses. Siena paid off the right people to operate. Kling, Pikus, and Louie asked Brucie if they could help him in anyway. He said everything was okay. They were thankful for the information and bought drinks for the house. They ordered and paid for fifteen cases of Puerto Rican Cerveza (beer) for their crews. Louie bought six bottles of gin, scotch, and whiskey. They almost bought Brucie's bar out. Dirty Neck and The Jib delivered the beer and whiskey to the dock where the Monroe was docked.

Brucie's real name was Bruce Jones. He was in the Navy ten years and discharged for the good of the service. He knew the islands in the Caribbean. While stationed at the Norfolk Navy Yard in his tenth year he was caught twice doing the Admiral's wives and also the daughters. So not to embarrass the Navy higher up officers and other people concerned it was a court martial or medical discharge. No pension or perks. Brucie took the medical discharge then went to the islands. He met Big Hattie in Puerto Rico. With what money he had saved while in the Navy he married Big Hattie and then bought the land on Pinero Island. It has been said that Brucie Jones was a good Warrant Officer. The trouble was he couldn't keep his trousers on. Big Hattie said, "I will keep his trousers on, I will keep the pump dry." Dirty Neck Harry and The Jib did a stretch in the Navy. The ILRP Officers taught Dirty Neck and The Jib how to make money the honest way. Take out fishing parties on their boats. Honest trading island to island also, to work for Brucie. Back on the Richey Commander Kling, Majors Pikus and Kling drank some beer in the wardroom. The crews of both boats had a beer party. In the wardroom Major Kling told Pikus and the Richey Commander, General Smith had told him the war clouds of Europe were booming. It would just take a spark. France had increased their antiquated bicycle army, England increased the Navy, and Germany increased the Army and Navy. The Germans are the best disciplined and trained Army. Colonel Byrnes' new assignment was recruiting twelve thousand men for the Marine Corps. The Army also needed ten thousand, the Navy two thousand, and the Coast Guard one thousand. Colonel Byrnes and his staff would travel to every state. The General wants Battalions -"B"- and -"C"- trained to a razor's edge. He said we will promote many Marines from Battalions -"B"- and -"C"- who qualify to sergeants. Commander Kling resumed his duties. Captain Sandy Cross took Majors Kling and Pikus back to their Battalions on Crab Island. All training was going on schedule.

Major Pikus was only one hour away from Kling's Battalion so he had his Sergeant pick up two horses and go with him to Kling's Battalion. He asked Kling when they were going to take care of Juan Siene's night club. Kling said, "Let's tackle this job on a weekend. We should be able to get all of them. The two of us, Louie, Eckert, Sambach, and about six Marines should do the job. Sandy Cross and his boat the Monroe are docked at San Juan. We will use his boat to get back and forth." The weekend for the raid on Juan Siena's night club was April 28, 29, and 30, 1913. Major Kling notified Sandy Cross about his part. Major Pikus picked six of the best revolver experts from his Battalion. Sandy Cross picked up the raiding party at 1500 hours on April 28. Most of the party spoke Spanish and were dressed like the local boys. They each had two hand grenades, knives, revolvers, and eighteen round of ammo. They landed on Ensenada Honda, Puerto Rico at 1730 hours. The eleven Marines split up. A guide from Sandy's crew was there to help them. One Marine and Lt. Eckert were to burn down the trading post on signal. Two Marines were to watch their backs and deep six anyone who tried to interfere. Three Marines were posted, two in the rear of the building and one in front to stop opposition. Majors Pikus and Kling, Louis, and Lt. Sambach would enter the nightclub. In the club a guide pointed out Juan Siena and his crew of killers. They were drinking with some girls. There were five of them with two guards with rifles. There was no why, where, or when. Kling, Pikus, Louie, and Sambach emptied their revolvers and killed the six men and Juan Siena. Everyone left the club. Only two men gave our rear guards a problem. The guards shot them. Grenades were set to go off at the pull of the cord. Lt. Eckert received the signal and Juan Siena and his empire was destroyed. By what right did the ILRP Unit Officers kill Juan Siena and his crew? In the Holy Bible –Life for Life- Eye for Eye. If you strike a mortal blow you must be put to death. Juan Siena and crew had murdered people before witnesses for no particular reasons.

They were wanted in three countries for murder and rape. Many countries have death squads. The ILRP Officers Units are not a death squad. They are a "Justice Squad". No con job lawyers or judges are needed. Criminals like Juan Siena should not be given a second chance. The world would be a safer place if we executed this type of criminal immediately after conviction. Majors Kling, Pikus and their staff returned to Crab Island. Their Battalions were fast becoming Four – 4.0.

Charles Sambach

Chapter 18

Battalions - "B"- and - "C"- were back to their home base in Quantico, Va. on July 2, 1913. Both Battalions were back on schedule. A parade was ordered for July 4, 1913. Past and review. Promotions for Battalions - "B"- and -"C"- would be announced.

Major Walter F. Kling
Major Edward Pikus
    to
Lieutenant Colonels

Captain Robert Zeke
Captain Bruce Wells
    to
Majors

Lt. Frank Eckert
Lt. Charles Sambach
to
Captains

Eight Marines who qualified were advanced to Sergeants, fifty to Corporals, and two hundred to Private First Class, ten First Sergeants were advanced to Gunnery Sgts. Colonel Byrnes was doing a good job of recruiting men for the Marines. The Marines at the present time did not have enough room at the training bases. Major Bryla was transferred to Parris Island, South Carolina to command Battalion - "G"-. Major John Conrad will train and command Battalion -"D"- at Remington, Va. Battalions -"G"- and -"D"- will each receive experience NCO's from the Battalions - "B"- and -"C"-. Battalion - "A"- and - "E"- will continue training at San Diego, California. The Fourth Marine Brigade T.O. six Battalions -"A-B-C-D-E-G"-. Three thousand Marines -"A"-"B-" Battalions – infantry - "C"- Battalion – mortars. "D" Battalion – machine guns. "E" Battalion – engineers, demolition, bridge structure, ordnance, communications. "G" Battalion – transportation, headquarters, communications, ammunition, supplies, military police. Supporting troops; twelve batteries of 105mm howitzers, twelve 75mm pack Howitzers, seventy hospital corpsmen, twenty-four doctors, three hundred service troops, food, grave registration, utilities. Brigade headquarters; two officers from each Battalion, twelve runners, twelve communication Marines. Colonel Walter Quick shall command the Fourth Marine Brigade. Lt. Colonels Kling and Pikus, Majors Zeke and Wells were ordered to report to ILRP Headquarters along with Captains Sambach and Eckert. General Smith and Colonel Dell Rico met with the six ILRP Officers on August 15, 1913 at ILRP Headquarters. The General said Kling, Zeke, and Eckert would attend a German language school for two months. Pikus, Wells, and Sambach would attend a French language school also for two months – August 17th to October 17th. After the sixty days of language schools the six officers will daily from October 20th to December 17th Monday to Friday from 1000 to 1600 hours attend lectures at the State Department on US Foreign Policy and Treaties, US Foreign Trade and Human Rights. The six Officers will receive furloughs from December 20th to January 5, 1914. They will report to ILRP Headquarters on January 6, 1914 at 1000 hours.

Wells, Zeke, Sambach, and Eckert all took off on December 21st to see friends, family, etc. Pikus and Kling were happy to be with their families. Kling's son was nine years old. Pikus' daughter was 10 years old. They each had two other children, one six year old daughter for Kling and one seven year old son for Pikus. Both of their wives were Nurse Supervisors at the hospital. Their wives only worked three days a week. Colonels Byrnes and Dell Rico were both on furlough until January 4, 1913. There was a lot of snow. The four families had a Happy Christmas and a New Year's Party.

Note: ILRP – Installation-Logistics-Resources-Program. Code words setup – supply of available future procedures. January 6, 1914 all Officers and personnel report in at ILRP Headquarters. Everyone immediately checked the bulletin board.

Officer's Fitness Reports Navy Hospital Quantico, Va.

January 8, 1914 – 1300 hours Colonels Byrnes and Dell Rico

January 9, 1914 – 1300 hours Lt. Colonels Kling and Pikus

January 10, 1914 – 1000 hours Majors Wells and Zeke, Captains Sambach and Eckert

January 13, 1913 – 1100 hours Unit I Personnel - guards, transportation, communication

January 14, 1914 – 1100 hours Unit II- guards, utilities, armory, housekeeping, office   military personnel

January 20, 1914 all Fitness Reports were in. There were a few minor exceptions. ILRP – 100% fitness.

Weapons qualifications

Rifles 1903 - .45 cal. pistol

Next bulletin for assignments

On January 22, 1914 a meeting was called for the six ILRP Officers to appear at the office of General Smith at 1400 hours. Colonels Byrnes and Dell Rico were also requested to attend. General Smith greeted the officers warmly. He said, "Let's get down to business. Colonel Dell Rico will remain my Aide- de -Camp. Colonel Byrnes will return to recruiting. The Marines will need five thousand men this year. A request had come to the State Department Office from England and France. They would like us to send two Army, Marine, and Naval Officers above the rank of Lieutenant to observe the training of Command Officers. Germany has also requested officers to observe their troops. What is going on? Are these countries trying to tell us something? It appears to the US Government that these countries have been mobilizing this past year. We will comply with all their requests. The information our officers pick up will help us serve our country. Captains Sambach and Eckert have this assignment. One month in each country. They will leave February 2nd return date June 15, 1914. Six days briefing before they leave." All out war was a real threat. Germany, Austria, Russia, and France. Lt. Colonels Kling and Pikus, Majors Zeke and Wells were

135

scheduled to report to Officer's code and Command School at Fort Belvoir, Virginia on February 1st to May 1, 1914. The Panama Canal was scheduled to open for traffic August 15, 1914. At the end of the meeting the General invited all to his brother's hotel for lunch.

May 17th Lt. Colonel Kling and Pikus returned to ILRP Headquarters. Majors Zeke and Wells reported to the rifle range at Quantico, Va. Kling and Pikus were to send the Marine units at ILRP Headquarters to the Quantico firing range for qualification of small arms. Three Marines daily including themselves between May 19th and June 15th, 1914. On June 20th General Smith will meet the Officers at ILRP Headquarters for assignments. Lt. Colonels Kling and Pikus, and Major Zeke were assigned to the Philippine Islands, Luzon and Mindanao where Guard Marine Companies were having trouble with the Moros and insurgents.

Kling and Pikus asked for three hundred Marines from Battalion "B"
Fourth Marine Brigade. They would also need the support of two 75 pack
Howitzer Batteries, twelve 37mm guns, 400 rounds of canister shot, one hundred fifty Marines who spoke or understood the Spanish dialect spoken on Luzon and Mindanao.
The Battalion was named -"H"-.
        T.O.
Six companies-
    Co. "A" - infantry-two hundred Marines
    Co. "B" - heavy weapons, machine guns, mortars, one hundred Marines
    Co. "E" - engineers, transportation, demolition, one hundred Marines
    Co. "D" - communications, headquarters, sixty Marines
    Co. "D" - ammunition, ordinance, supplies, equipment, one hundred
    Marines
    Co. "F"- Marines, mess, one hundred Navy Medical Corpsmen,

Doctors, Chaplin
Battalion -"H"- Personnel -824- Supply and Troopship,
Troopship
Merrill, supply Henderson, one Navy oiler, one ammo
and coal ship, Naval support Flotilla I, Commander
Frank   E. Kling, six Destroyers – Richey -387, Jones
-388, Smith-389, Johnson-390, Lee-391, Wood-392
Port of departure – Norfolk, Virginia
August 16, 1914 – 1600 hours
Germany, Austria, Russia, France declared World War I
August 16, 1914.

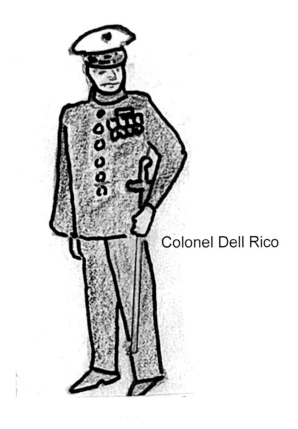

Colonel Dell Rico

Chapter 19

All ships were to clear the Panama Canal by August 23rd and head for San Diego. Three day stop over at San Diego then to Pearl Harbor, Hawaii. Ten days at Pearl Harbor. Eight Marines who spoke the dialects of the islands were assigned to each company.

Company T.O. one Lieutenant 2nd Class, four Sergeants, four Corporals, eighty-one Pfc.s and Privates, four Navy Corpsmen.
Marines: mixed units, machine guns, communications, mortars, engineers, and transportation, medical. The Destroyer Jones-388 with full Marine equipment, ammo, food will land first at Glan, Mindanao Island. The Jones will then patrol the area of Davao gulf. The Marines will move north to Digas. They will deep six any Moros or insurgents causing trouble. The Destroyer Smith-389 with the same number of Marines and equipment will land at Lebak with one 75mm pack Howitzer. The Wood-392 will land the same number of Marines and equipment at Hijo, Mindanao. The Lee-391 will land its units on Mati. All units will clear and destroy known places of trouble makers. They will deep six insurgents and Moros causing death and destruction. No prisoners will be taken. All Marines will carry three hand grenades. Destroyers off shore will keep on communications with their units by semaphore, runners, flags, and Morse code. The rest of the Battalion will be landed at Davao on the island of Mindanao, Philippines. All units will head north to Davao, Mindanao after clearing their areas.

It took the landing units ten days to clear their areas before they could report to Davao Battalion Headquarters. A good area with water was picked for the Battalion camp. Tents, mess halls, heads, and showers were set up for the companies reporting in. The companies needed a good feeding, medical care, and showers. It was now September 30, 1914. The Battalion was reformed. Casualties had been light on the search and destroy mission. Only forty casualties; fifteen dead and twenty-five wounded.

Now every Marine is a rifleman. Rank or other position in the corps is secondary. Replacements on the line sometimes are cook, bakers, and truck drivers. To be called a Marine in 1914 you would have to qualify with the 1903 Springfield rifle and not be afraid to draw blood with the knife and bayonet, no retreat.

October 5, 1914 "H" Battalion moved out to complete the search and destroy mission on Mindanao. Before the Battalion moved out native scouts from the American Army reported that about eight hundred insurgents and Moros occupied the town of Cagayan. A lot of boats were in the water outside the town. Cagayan was northwest of Davao and a seaport on the Sulu Sea. Commander Kling was ordered by the Navy Department to proceed with three destroyers and patrol the Philippine Sea near the island of Catanduanes. They were to keep eight Japanese ships under surveillance. The Japanese Government had notified the U.S. Government of their ships on maneuvers. One could say the Japanese were a little off course for maneuvers. Commander Kling asked Louie to join his second in command with the Destroyers Johnson, Lee, and Woods for a Marine landing on the coast of Cagayan.

Lt. Colonel Kling's and Pikus' attack plan was to land one hundred fifty Marines with full equipment on the beach of Cagayan. They would fight and clear the area toward the town and hold a line until the rest of the Battalions moved up from the south and west. Louie without permission from the Lt. in charge said he was going with the Marines. Some Marines remembered the help Louie gave them with the machine gun in the Caribbean areas. Louie was a Lieutenant and there was no limit of his friendship with Kling and Pikus. They had experienced Louie in action.

Fifteen minutes before landing the Destroyers Lee, Wood, and Johnson would shell the beach and the outside area with four shrapnel and two smoke shells. As Kling and Pikus were checking their attack plan the Duty Sergeant came in the tent and said that a Philippine Army scout asked for Kling and

Pikus. The Army scout said two hundred of his unit, U.S. Army and Philippine scouts were slaughtered. A surprise attack. He believed six hundred Moros and insurgents attacked them at 0200 hours. He was one of twenty that escaped getting killed. He said the Moros and insurgents had about fifteen hundred men around Cagayan, also about three hundred boats. Pikus said to Kling, "We will have to change some of our attack plans. We will have to commit the entire Battalion. Everyone will get a rifle." Kling said, "We will start our attack two days from now." The three Destroyers on the morning of October 14th at 0600 hours will destroy all the boats they can find on the water and shore of Cagayan. The Destroyers each will shell the beach and town with six rounds of H.E. Shrapnel and two smoke shells. The Destroyers will then retreat six miles out and wait for instructions. On the morning of October 15th the three Destroyers will again come in and shell the town and area of Cagayan with ten shrapnel and two smoke shells then retreat out of range. On October 16th at 0500 hours the Destroyers will rake the beaches, port, and town for fifteen minutes with the shells allotted for this campaign.

The Battalion had been formalized for combat at Cagayan, Mindanao Island in the Philippines. Company -"A"- with Major Wells in command and two hundred Marine riflemen will move in from the east with two machine guns and three 37 mm guns. He will move in to 37 mm range and rake with canister shot when he hears the signal. Company -"B"- with major Zeke in command will support Company -"A"- moving in from the southeast with one hundred fifty riflemen, two machine guns, one battery of 75mm packs, and three 37mm guns. Zeke's battery of 75mm packs will start shelling when he is in range. He will hold back on the 37mm until he hears the signal. Lt. Colonel Pikus will move in with the company -"C"- from the southwest with two hundred Marines, riflemen, two machine guns, and three 37mm guns. Lt. Colonel Kling will be in the Command of company -"E"- with one hundred Marines and will attack on signal from the front of boundary line of Cagayan. His battery of 75mm packs will concentrate on clearing an area for a front attack. Lt. Colonel Kling is overall commander of the campaign.

Kling told all of his company commanders the signal would be Red Smoke when all the 37mm guns were in range to rake the Moros and insurgents. When they bunch together in any formations, waves, or groups tell your Marines to use hand grenades.

Captain Eckert-Communication Officer, Company -"D"- Reserve Captain Sambach in command- one hundred twenty- five Marines and one hundred Navy personnel (doctors, corpsmen) and some service Marines.

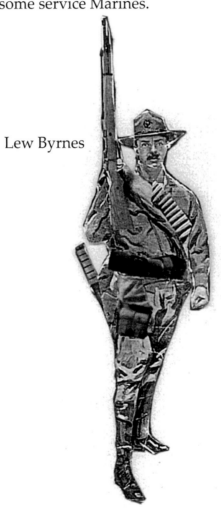

Lew Byrnes

Chapter 20

The three Destroyers moved in again and shelled the shore line and anything that looked like a defensive building or trench line. Every company saw the red smoke. The two batteries of 75 packs went into action. The twelve 37mm guns with canister shot was light artillery. It cut the enemy in pieces. The attacking rifle Marines threw hand grenades like they were going out of style. They used their rifles and bayonets. The Moros and insurgents fought back viciously with bolos, rifles, swords, and knives. We broke their backs with our 75mm packs and canister shot. The battle raged in our favor. Lt. Colonel Kling received a message stating three hundred of the enemy fled north to the coast town of Surigao. The message was telegraphed to Commander Frank E. Kling. If he was in the clear to stand off Surigao, Mindanao and stop any evacuation by boat. Lt. Colonel Kling did not want any of the enemy to get out of Mindanao alive. The next campaign was the island of Luzon. The Marines swept over the enemy and town. What a mess of dead, dying, and wounded. All the wounded enemies were destroyed. Nine hundred enemy were killed.

Casualties – Marines – Navy

Company -"A"- fifty dead, thirty-five wounded

Company -"B"- sixty dead, twenty-one wounded

Company -"C"- twenty dead, thirty-nine wounded

Company -"E"- forty-five dead, twenty wounded

Total battle casualties Battalion -"H"- 175 dead, 115 wounded

The Battalion now had five hundred sixty-four Marines and twenty corpsmen to finish the job on Mindanao Island. The wounded would be taken out by Destroyers to the Army Hospital at Manila. Army Grave Registration would take care of the dead Marines and Navy men. Lt. Colonel Kling telegraphed the Pacific Marine Command requesting three hundred replacement Marines and twenty-five Navy corpsmen for the Luzon campaign. Commander F. Kling's

Destroyers could pick up the Marines from the smaller detachments on other Philippine Islands, Panay, Samar, and Mindanao.

To Lt. Colonel Walter F. Kling
Cagayan, Mindanao.
From Pacific Area Marine Command

No replacements of Marines available. One hundred U.S. Army and two hundred U.S. Army trained Philippine Scouts, your replacement waiting at U.S. Army Barracks Camp More, Manila.

Kling did not expect any help to complete the Mindanao Campaign. The Marines as well as the U.S. Government expected miracles from the ILRP Marine Officers. Kling and Pikus decided on two columns of Marines. Two hundred Marines in each column to finish the campaign at Surigao, Mindanao. Never thinking they could be defeated they completed their plans. Kling would be in reserve with one hundred sixty-four Marines and Navy personnel. Pikus would attack along and forward on the east coast. Major Zeke would attack along the west coast and forward. If Commander Frank Kling got his message and could do some shelling of the enemy's position everything should work out. Pikus' and Zeke's Marines were one quarter of a mile outside the town of Surigao. There was lots of sniping along the march to their present position. Caualties: Pikus – two dead and Zeke three dead Marines. Colonel Kling was one half mile back from the two columns. Major Wells was now in command of the Reserve Troops. Kling picked up twenty U.S. Army men and forty Philippine Army Scouts. He decided he wanted to get into the fight. He called for Captains Eckert and Sambach to come up. He gave thirty of the men to Sambach and thirty to Eckert. Two platoons. He said, "We are going forward and knock hell out of the enemy." He wasn't kidding. Hell was Kling's name.

Sambach's platoon had one 30 cal. machine gun and one 37mm gun with canister shot. The troops also had rifles, bayonets, and hand grenades. It was October 29, 1914. The

143

attack started at 0600 on the morning of October 30, 1914. Pikus and Zeke had their batteries of 75mm working until they ran out of shells. They next used their 37mm with canister shot. Their Marines with rifles and bayonet went in. It was a bloody fight with bolos and knives against the Marines with bayonets. Lt. Colonel Pikus was cut on the left arm and leg. The corpsmen quickly took him out of the fight for treatment as well as other wounded Marines. Zeke was wounded in the left shoulder and cut on the right leg. The Marines killed and killed and were killed. Colonel Kling, Captains Sambach, and Eckert charged in with their sixty men and went to work. Shooting and stabbing was the name of the game. Kling was creased on his left ear and received cuts on his right arm. His men gave no quarters. The fighting went on until the Marines made sure all the enemy were killed.

Enemy dead 350 – no prisoners
Attacking Force Casualties:
Marines - one hundred fifty-one dead
One hundred wounded
U.S. Army - ten dead - five wounded
Battalion -"H"- Strength
November 1, 1914
Marines 243
Navy 70

On November 3, 1914 a small hospital ship docked at Port Surigao and took the most severely wounded to the U.S. Army Hospital in Manila. Commander Kling was able to take some of the lighter casualties. After the Battle of Davao the Destroyers Wood, Lee, and Johnson went to Manila to be resupplied with ammo, food, and fuel. They then returned to Port Surigao with one hundred U.S. Army soldiers and one hundred fifty Philippine Scout soldiers for island security on Mindanao. One post was in the north and another in the south of the island.

Lieutenant Louie did not take part in any of the battles. He couldn't get off his ship. General Smith telegraphed Kling and Pikus for them to send their reports. He did receive one report from Marine Pacific Command. Kling and Pikus would be laid up for at least three weeks.

There was a lot of action in the hills north of Manila. There was only one Battalion of Army and Philippine Scouts to hold the area stable. The present Philippine Government estimated about three thousand Moros and insurgents were causing the trouble trying to take back the Philippine Islands and Government.

The United States Government did not have enough soldiers or Marines at this time to reinforce any of the islands, possessions, or territories outside of the USA. There was trouble with Mexico, in the Caribbean, Nicaragua, Haiti, and the Dominican Republic. German ships tried to dock at Antigua. They war in Europe that started around July or August, 1914 was giving the U.S. government a lot to think about. What troops the United States had in the Philippines would have to take care of their problems. We also had to take care of the Panama Canal that had just opened August 14, 1914 and there was also trouble along the Mexican border.

Chapter 21

November, 1914 U.S. Army Hospital Manila, Luzon Island, Philippines. Kling and Pikus had serious cuts that needed much stitching. Their bodies hurt and they were in pain and they both had fevers. They were both worried about their officers and Marines. November 14th Pikus and Kling were feeling better. Pikus asked how many of the Marines had made it. The Head Surgeon said it was possible forty-six should make it. Twenty died of wounds and the rest would receive a medical discharge when they are returned to the Marine and Navy Hospital in Quantico, Virginia. Letters and packages came in daily. They were busy trying to answer family mail. Island Military Officers came in to talk to them. The Head Surgeon told them to leave and come back in two weeks. The Head Surgeon said he was very satisfied with the way their wounds were healing. Some of the stitching threads were removed from both of their arms and legs and the facial cuts were healing. On November 25, 1914 Lt. Colonel Kling received communication by letter delivered by a U.S. Army Sergeant. He had to sign for it. The Sergeant said he was told to stay at the hospital for one hour in the event of a reply. Looking over the letter Kling called for the Sergeant and told him, "No reply." The letter was from U.S. Army Headquarters Camp More, Manila, Luzon. The letter said Kling's Marines, 385 of them with 100 U.S. Army and 150 Philippine soldiers were training together. The Army has transferred Battalion -"B"- and -"C"- from the "28th" Division Schofield Barracks, Hawaii. -"B"- Battalion soldiers will be replacements for Army outpost on other islands. - "C"- Battalion with the permission of Three Star Army General Phinas the Marines will have including Battalion -"H"- nine hundred thirty Marines and soldiers to clean out the North section of Luzon Island.

December 4, 1914 Kling and Pikus were released from the hospital. They passed the fitness examination so the record said. They both were glad to get back to the battalion. They still were not 100% healthy. Wells, Zeke, and Sambach were not 100% either. At Camp More Pikus, Kling, and Lieutenant Kellstrom from the Army started making plans for the Northern Luzon Campaign. By agreement Kling was Senior Spokesman. Kling said they should start by sending one hundred and fifty Marine and Army units north from Manila to Regate. They would need commander Kling's Flotilla of six destroyers. They had the experience on this type of operation. One destroyer would land two hundred of Army and Marine companies on Aparri, North Luzon. This company will then move south under the Command of Major Wells and his senior officers. This will be called company - "B"-. A company of Marines and Army – two hundred men will be called Company - "C"- under the command of Major Zeke and will land at Vigano. Captain Eckert will command Company -"G"- and land a company of two hundred Army and Marines at Tuquegarao. At the signal Major Wells' command will remove all opposition, Moros, insurgents, and move south to meet Major Zeke's Co. -"C"-. The three companies -"B"-, - "C"-, and -"G"- will work together and clean out the Moros and insurgents at Bontuco, Hagan, San Fernando, and Bagnia. They will meet with the reserve company for replacements and ammo at Lingayen. Captain Sanbach's command that moved north from Manila will meet up with the three companies. The reserve company of one hundred fifty-five men will remain at Lingayen. A branch of it will be headquarters. Three hundred Philippine Army Scouts have been added to the command Battalion -"H"-; they will clean up San Idefonzo, Tarlao, Cabanatvan, and Iba. Commander Kling's Destroyers will be at designated areas to pickup the wounded and dead. All wounded will go to the Army Hospital in Manila. This campaign started December 10th 1914 and was considered very successfully completed on March 20, 1915.

Casualties - Battalion -"H"-

U.S. Marines	89 dead
	94 wounded
U.S. Army	91 dead

147

	104 wounded
Philippine Scouts Army	125 dead
	200 wounded
Muros	915 known dead
	375 wounded
Philippine Insurgents	475 known dead
	275 wounded

All wounded Moros and insurgents were shot. The Philippine Army, Navy, and Coast Guard were growing and should now be able to hold their elected Government in office. The United States will be the protectorate of the Philippine Islands. Kling and Pikus had to remain in Manila to straighten out the Marine's dead, wounded, and other problems. Commander Kling's Flotilla was leaving for the United States on April 3, 1915. Lt. Colonels Pikus, Kling, Majors Zeke and Wells, Captains Sambach and Eckert, and one hundred thirty Marines that survived the campaign were passengers. Commander Kling said that we would have to stop at Pearl Harbor, Hawaii for fuel and supplies. We moved into an empty destroyer slip at Pearl Harbor. The Commander said that we would be here for five days liberty - two days starboard watch then two days port watch.

Pikus and Kling decided to get a hotel room on the beach. The only room they could get was a two bedroom suite. For Navy men it was twenty-five dollars a night. They took it for three nights. The "Mellawanna Hotel" where they stayed had allowed a movie company to make a movie picture on the property. They heard it was called "Hawaiian Love Song". Kling said, "Now I know why we were lucky to get this room." No one wanted it. It was close to the movie set. The movie set was from Hollywood, California. Starring in the movie was Jean Gayner, Eileen Binfeld, and Charles Bickford also, Three Fingers Brown and One Eye Jones. This meant nothing to Pikus and Kling. They never saw a movie. They were told it was the last day of the movie making. No more noise! A party was scheduled for the Navy Officers the second night of their stay. Commander Kling knew many officers at the party and he introduced Kling and Pikus to an Admiral named Smalley. Kling later said he remembered that Smalley helped to ouster Brucie from the Navy. Brucie was doing his wife and daughter. (That's Caribbean Brucie the one married to Big Hattie.) It was a great party, "Bing, Bang, Boom"! Every one got drunk. Kling and Pikus were introduced to Kirsten and Iris. They paired off dancing, drinking, feeling, and then some. This was madness! The next morning Kling woke up with Kirsten in bed, Pikus woke up with Iris. "Did we diddle?" Pikus asked. Both of the girls laughed. They both had that hungry look in their eyes that Pikus and Kling saw at the dance. These girls were bound to score. They liked young good-looking Marines. Pikus said to Kling, "We are worth it. We've been through hell." Pikus and Kling stayed in their rooms grab assing around until 1300 hours. They cooled off with a shower. Kirsten telephoned her chauffeur to pick them up at 1500 hours. The girls treated them to dinner and drinks at Nero's Steak House. At 1900 hours Kirsten told the chauffeur to take them to Guard Gate 4 Pearl Harbor. Pikus told the girls they had had a first class time. Both girls still had that hungry look in their eyes. They kissed the girls. After returning the Gate Guards's salute they walked to the Richey's berth. They then remembered they had to pick up their clothes at the hotel. They went off the wagon once.

It was now April 18th 1915 and they were on their way to San Diego, California. Commander Kling's Flotilla was ordered to Norfolk, Virginia. It took Kling's destroyers fourteen days to get to Norfolk. All of his destroyers needed work. Admiral Jones said he would do his best for base guard duty and training for Commander Kling's flotilla. His crews would have to be trained on new guns and do base guard duty. Also, experienced men will have to be found and trained to replace Kling's casualties.

Chapter 22

Commander Kling said he was going to take a vacation, maybe get married. He had a thirty days furlough coming. He met Major Bryla's sister at a party two years ago and they had been corresponding by letter for one year. The Navy Dept. Admiral Jones said Kling was ready for a cruiser command. Commander Kling went off to Orange, New Jersey to see Major Bryla's sister. Her name was Rebecca. Major Bryla was on furlough and he was happy to see the Commander. The Bryla's had a large family. Major Bryla and the Commander each rented a room at the YMCA in Orange. After going out for two weeks Rebecca and Kling decided to get married. Rebecca's brother had a car they were able to drive around in. A small family wedding was arranged. It would have to do for now. Before the marriage Kling told Rebecca he was Navy all the way like his brother who was a Marine all the way. The Commander telephoned his brother Lt. Colonel Kling at ILRP Headquarters and asked his brother to look for a lot approximately 100 x 100 in his neighborhood. He said he was married and asked if he and his bride could be a guest for a few days. Colonel Kling told Colonel Pikus and PIkus said, "We take care of our own." Commander Kling and his bride will find food and shelter from the inseparables. The Commander and his bride had a five day honeymoon in Washington D.C. They went to his brother's house. It was now May 25, 1915. Kling and Pikus gave a big party for the newly married couple. Pikus and Kling also found a secretarial job in the Navy Department for the new bride. "O Happy Day!" She will start work on June 20th at the Navy Department Section 101. The Commander had to report to the Naval Shipyard Norfolk, Virginia June 7, 1915 at 0900 hours. Colonels Kling and Pikus found a lot for the Commander after he had to leave. Rebecca and the Commander said they would like to build a three bedroom two bath ranch, all on one floor. The Commander asked his brother if he could take care of the early stages of building, he would leave money and authorization.

He was ordered to take his Flotilla immediately on a shake down cruise. He would be out of the country about two weeks. Commander Kling's Flotilla took three weeks to get in shape. He had some trouble with the new four and five inch guns, batteries, also, the small gun turrets. With new men in the Flotilla (six destroyers) repetitious training on gunnery was "do or die". With Louie and the Commander you had to be a top grade sailor, marking of shells, fuses, magazines, powder, primers, and the nomenclature of parts of guns. Top priority! It was May1, 1915 and schooling on the Flotilla was daily from 0900 to 1500 hours then guard duty or other duties. Commander Kling was able to get away for a day or two to check on his new home being built in Alexandria, Virginia. His lot was on a street in back of his brother's house. His wife was happy working at the Navy Department. She would also take care of Colonels Pikus' and Kling's children when needed.

On May 8 the news came over the radio that a German submarine sunk the British ship Lusitania. Many Americans were on the ship. Over one thousand passengers lost their lives. Germany said they would sink any British ships if American citizens were on it. The U.S. President decided to protect British and American ships. Commander Kling's well trained Flotilla would have the honor of escorting three British and two American Cargo ships to England. July 26, 1915 Commander Kling's Flotilla was waiting outside New York Harbor for the ship's escort. Kling was told when they reached Liverpool, England his Flotilla would be docked for approximately three weeks. Training, signals, ship information, escort duty, German subs and exchange information on English and German Naval ships. Kling and Louie's study of German sub attacks and the German Navy were noted and the reports would be turned over to the U.S. Navy Dept. They hoped to be home by August 31, 1915. They would escort three American cargo ships and one passenger liner to America.

Norfolk, Newport News, Virginia September 1, 1915 Unit I

Commander Kling's Flotilla was moored on the James River. Orders were waiting for Commander Kling and Lt. Louie. After turning in their reports the Marine Orderly told them to go to Admiral W.C. Scott's office in Building 1. After saluting the O.D. in charge they were escorted to the Admiral's Office. The Admiral greeted them and said they had done a great job on the first cargo ship Navel escort. The Chief of Naval Operations ordered Commander Kling, his destroyers Richey, Jones, and Lee to stay on escort duty and each trip train three new crews and officers. Kling and Louie turned in much needed information received from the British on German submarines. This was called "Training while on the job" from New York or Boston to Liverpool, England. Louie now a Senior Lieutenant would be in charge of three destroyers: The Smith-387, James-388, and Able-389. The Able would be headquarters for the Flotilla and would patrol from Havana, Cuba to Trinidad, Canal Zone, and Corn Island, Nicaragua to Pregree, Mexico. Assignment - German or other European intervention. Hunt any foreign submarines - check ships. Commander Kling and Lt. Louie did not like the split but the present situation called for it. Kling and Louie were together so long they hated to part. They both went back to their assignments very unhappy.

Commandant Smith asked Colonel Dell Rico to check and see if all the ILRP Officers were back at their headquarters. He said congratulations were in order to Colonel Dell Rico on his promotion to Brigadier General. He said Brigadier General Dell Rico would remain in Washington as his Liaison Officer to police and strengthen the Corps. The Commandant said he would meet with the six senior officers of the ILRP at their Headquarters September 2, 1915. After the meeting he said there would be a party at his brother's hotel for Colonel Dell Rico. The announcement - Promotion to Brigadier General. The meeting at the ILRP Headquarters was scheduled for 1000 hours August 2nd.

September 2, 1915 - meeting ILRP Headquarters Commandant Smith opened the meeting. He said we have bad news from the South Atlantic and Caribbean areas. The Haitian bandits are trying to destroy everything we built up in Haiti. The Dominican Republic has the same problem. The Nicaraguan problem gets frightening. The 4th and 5th Marine Regiments are well trained and they have the equipment and are ready to move on a day's notice. "I cannot use them for the Caribbean problems. They are ready made for the big event I believe is going to happen soon. We have hundreds of young Marines with only four or five months training for the Caribbean campaign. Colonel Kling, Major Zeke, and Captain Eckert will have to handle the Haiti problem with three hundred boot Marines, some new junior officers will be added. The three ILRP Marine Senior Officers will get this job done. They will train the Marines on the job. Colonel Pikus, Major Wells, and Captain Sambach will tackle the Dominican Republic problem. You people I know can do the job. You will also have three hundred boot Marine and Officers. Colonel Kling's Marines will be noted as Unit 1-USMC, Colonel Pikus' as Unit II-USMC. You Senior Officers have the life over death "judge and jury". You six officers are the United States best in Duty, Judge, and Jury."

It is a shame these small protectorates have these problems of insurgents and bandits in their countries. There are a lot of good people in both countries. The U.S. knows some European insurgents start the trouble to keep the United States from seeing what they are doing in Europe and other places. The war starting on August 4, 1914 was a big problem. The European countries were taking sides and they would no doubt need material and supplies from the United States. The U.S. was not in the war at this time but was having trouble with the Mexican and European spies.

Chapter 23

It was known at this time, July 25, 1915, that Commander Kling, Lt. Louie, Colonels Kling and Pikus had Caribbean Brucie apply for reinstatement in the U.S. Navy. He filled out an application of his history since being discharged. Brucie had a good eight year record. He was out of the Navy just a few years, thirty-four years of age and believed to be in good health. Brucie knew the South Atlantic and Caribbean areas; he also knew the good people and the bad people - an asset to the Navy. He was also a natural for command of our two gun boats, the Monroe and the Doctrine. Between escort trips to Europe Commander Kling was asked to attend a U.S. Naval meeting in Washington D.C. He had the opportunity to talk to Admirals Jones, Scott, and Paterson. They also said after reviewing Brucie's case they thought he had gotten a raw deal from the Navy. He should not have been discharged for so minor a charge. They would get him reinstated. Brucie would have to report to Admiral Jones' office at Norfolk, Va. He would have to pass an entrance exam and health fitness. The Admiral said they noticed Brucie had citations and had been very useful in South American waters. His service had been on destroyers. When Brucie received the letter from Admiral Jones he immediately made plans to travel to Virginia. He told Hattie she was now in complete charge of their business. "Everything you do Hattie has to be on the good side. I want you to build up a hotel and fishing club for vacation people. No shady business." He said Hattie, "I was always a Navy man and will be home now and then." He looked for some old books and started to study. Brucie received a second letter from Admiral Jones. He was to report to Jones' office no later than August 10, 1915 at 0900 hours Navy building Norfolk, Va. The Navy gave Brucie ten days to study for the entrance examination. He studied, ate, and slept at the Petty Officer's quarters. On August 23, 1915 the three day oral and written tests were over. One more day for the medical. On August 28, 1915 Brucie was enlisted as a Chief Petty Ordinance Officer

1st Grade. Machinists and communication was also added to his rate. He would have to have nine months sea duty and pass the Bureau of Navigation Standard Test, Geometry, Chemistry, and Physics tests to be commissioned a Second Lieutenant. He could study as he did his duty as a Chief Petty Officer. August 31st Chief Brucie was ordered to San Juan, Puerto Rico Navy Yard as First Mate on the Gunship Monroe. Captain Crow was still in command of the gunships Monroe and Doctrine now at Pier II P.R. Navy Yard. The Lieutenant in Command of the Doctrine came down with a bad case of Malaria. He was being shipped to the States. Captain Crow knew Brucie for years. He put Brucie in command of the Doctrine. He gave Brucie four days leave to see Hattie. Hattie had Dirty Neck Harry and the Jib working their asses off. She wouldn't give them time to breathe. Brucie's children were in good health. He loved Hattie in his own way. Hattie loved him passionately. Hattie was going to make her part of the island respectable and she had the muscle to do it. Brucie told Harry and the Jib to play it straight or else! Brucie said he would make amends to people he had hornswoggled.

On September 10, 1915 the Commandant of the Marine Corps ordered Colonel Kling, Major Zeke, Captain Eckert, and Unit 1 USMC to Haiti. Colonel Pikus, Major Wells, Captain Sambach, and Unit II USMC were ordered to the Dominican Republic. Each unit had one hundred and fifty horse Marines and one hundred fifty Mud Marines - six month recruits, twenty-five corpsmen, and two doctors. Both units had full equipment.

Minimum Weapons - Ammunition
8- machine guns - .38 cal.
4- pack 75 mm - 125 rounds
8- 31 mm guns - 200 canister-100-AP
6- 60 mm mortars - 100 MS
450- .03 Springfield rifles
Bayonets
35 cases of hand grenades
25 thousand rounds .30 cal.
5 thousand 45 cal. Ammo

150 rolls barbed wire

175 horses

25 pack mules

Because of the war in Europe ammo and weapons were not plentiful.

On September 18, 1915 at 0530 hours twenty-five Marines with Major Zeke made a beach head landing two miles north of Port-au-Prince. They moved inland about one half mile and were not opposed. Captain Eckert landed with twenty-five Marine engineers who looked over the flat dry land reported by the scouts. The engineers laid out and started to set up a camp site. Equipment was brought in. The horse Marine scouts checked out one mile in each direction, no opposition. First aid tent, mess tent, and Colonel's Headquarters tent were set up. Tent rows, heads, and outside wash basins were set up. Trenches were dug. Barbed wire was stretched around the camp site with grenade traps. There were only two ways to get out of the camp site without getting hurt or killed. The four corners of the camp each had 30 cal. machine gun and a 37 mm gun. Twenty-four hour sentry duty around the clock and a fire watch, daily horse Marine patrol one mile outside of camp in all directions. Communications with Lt. Louie's destroyers, gun boats, and San Juan was a problem.

On September 21st at 0400 hours many rifle shots killed two of the sentries on the north corner of the camp. The sentry on the machine gun south corner swept the area where the shots came from. It then became quiet right into dawn. The only damage to the camp - two dead Marines. On September 22nd the horse patrol that was checking north of the camp picked up two Haitians who said they were trustworthy villagers. They said guerillas and bandits about three hundred of them were camped outside of Petite Riviere. They were going to attack the Americano camp. Kling and his horse patrol took the two Haitians back to their village to check them out. The village had been threatened by the guerillas who wanted all the food they could get. The villagers asked the Marines for help. The camp was not yet completed. Outside communications were not good. Colonel Kling decided to attack the guerillas. He was informed they were getting together in one area. No fortification. He formed a two hundred Marine Unit with four machine guns, four 37 mm guns, canister shot, two seventy-five packs, and three 60 mm mortars. Each Marine carried two hand grenades. One hundred twenty-five horse Marines - cavalry, seventy-five mud Marines. Fifty horse Marines with Major Zeke in command were able to get within five hundred yards of the guerillas. No outer guards. The guerillas were drinking, eating, and playing around with some girls. No fortification.

Zeke said to his Lieutenant that this could be a trap. It was no trap. These guerillas got together by a leader named Gene Charlose. They thought the U.S. Marines were over rated. "Boy! Did they think wrong?" Zeke placed his machine guns and 37 mm guns covering the area where most of them were together. The horses had been left back about a quarter of a mile. The Marines crept close. It was now twenty-three hundred hours. Kling told Captain Eckert to secure the camp. One hundred Marines were left at the camp with one doctor and ten corpsmen. One hundred mud Marines and fifty horse Marines started traveling to the attack area to meet Major Zeke. Kling's attack force made the ten mile trip and was ready to go into action at 0500 hours. The next morning these young Marines wanted blood. The attack started at 0600 hours. It was September 25, 1915. Kling's two 75 mm packs went into action and took out all the horses, five houses, and one large building that was their headquarters, whore house, and bar. His 37 mm with canister shot and machine guns slaughtered the guerillas. The one hundred mud Marines went in with bayonets and rifles firing followed by fifty horse Marines with sabers flashing. "What a charge!"

Two hundred and seventy-five male guerillas were killed. Thirty-five wounded. The wounded were shot. Fifteen women and two children were dead. Marine casualties were twenty mud Marines, and five Horse Marines dead. Ten Mud Marines and three Horse Marines wounded. Kling left twenty-five Mud Marines and a Lieutenant to bury the dead guerillas. The dead Marines were taken back to the base camp for burial. Communications was open at the base camp. Colonel Kling received a message from the Navy Dept. Washington D.C. to start building. The base camp was going to be a permanent Constabulary for a Military Armed Police Force. Kling received a second message. The Commandant shipped thirty-five horses and twenty-five mud Marines to the Constabulary with much needed building supplies. Colonel Kling recruited twenty-five male Haitians who he believed would be an asset to the horse Marine Patrols. They had a language problem. They spoke Haitian, French, or Pig Haitian English. Patrols went out daily to villages checking for bandits, guerillas, or settling the villager's problems. Colonel Kling received a third message from the Commandant. One of Lt. Louie's destroyers would pick him up. He was to go to Cape Haitian area and set up a second Constabulary. Major Zeke would be Commanding Officer of the Port-au-Prince Constabulary.

Chapter 24

The Destroyer Able, Lt. Louie's headquarters had to drop anchor one quarter of a mile from the dock off Cape Haitien. The USS Merrill supply ship was unloading building materials and other supplies on the pier. Colonel Kling was taken into shore by a small boat. Kling walked up to the dock to the roadway and was surprised to meet Major Bryla. Bryla landed at Cape Haitien with two hundred Marines and twenty Navy Corpsmen. One hundred of them were horse Marines. Bryla's engineers mapped out an area one half mile inland near a stream. Bryla called for two horses for them to ride up to the camp site. Colonel Kling looked over the site Major Bryla had selected. Kling said he liked the site. He said the reason he was here was to find a site for a permanent constabulary. "You found it." Kling explained his orders from the Navy Dept., Washington, D.C. Kling said, "We have to pacify the Haitians and show good will. We need their support to stop the terrorists, guerillas, and agitation. We have to help this country firmly establish a peacekeeping militia." Kling helped Major Bryla to set up the Constabulary. Bryla had six villages he was told to visit. The Junior Officers in Major Bryla's unit had no experience in the Caribbean areas. Colonel Kling said he would take care of visiting villages and establishing good will and trust. He knew the villages. All had bandit trouble. The French Haitians and Pig Latin English was a big problem. Kling found four Haitians that worked on the pier. They spoke some English and were interested in a Haitian militia. The first village Kling said he would visit was Mance. It was twenty-five miles away from the Constabulary. He would need:

75 horse Marine platoon
4 Navy Corpsmen
75 45 cal. 25 rounds each
.03 Springfield rifles 90 rounds each
Cavalry swords and bayonets
2 machine guns - 30 cal.

2 37mm guns - 300 canister rounds
75 first aid kits, canteens, mess gear
1 blanket and 1 poncho each
2 lariats each and 25 feet rope #2
2 hand grenades for each man
2 cases hand grenades
3 axes and 3 shovels
60 shelter halfs with pegs
12 days rations for each Marine
35 horses, 5 pack horses, 12 pack mules, and feed
3 mortars - 60mm
750 45 cal. round ammo
3000 rounds 30 cal. ammo
3 75 pack Howitzers

Kling said, "We have to go prepared. We will be challenged, ambushed, and assaulted by insurgents. We also should have communication with Louie's destroyers and our gunboats either by flag, semaphore, mirrors, light, or signal telegraph Morse code." Marines were told never to retreat just fight in another direction.

October 15, 1915 was a rainy windy day. Colonel Kling said they would wait a few days for the rain to stop then start the patrol. Two of the four Haitians asked if they could be scouts and have rifles. Kling said maybe after I give you a fast course on field scouting. Rain was expected for two days. Kling told his platoon to rest, chow up, and check their clothes and equipment. On the second day of rain Kling had his platoon together and told them to keep their teeth and bodies as clean as they could. He told them to use their mosquito nets and to check the ground before they lay down for Myriapop centipedes and scorpions. No smoking, loud talking, or singing while on patrol. Don't forget your enemy can smell cigar and cigarette smoke, a dead give away. Bury your garbage. Keep your horses brushed and clean. Keep on the alert and don't sleep while on watch because the throat they cut may be yours.

October 25, 1915 the advance scouts started the patrol at

0800 hours. The rest of the patrol followed two hours later. The platoon traveled along the coast for about ten miles then started inland. About two mile inland shots were fired at the patrol. No one was hit. The patrol was at rest. An advance scout brought in a dead male. He said, "This person was the one who fired at you." He also had the rifle. The patrol continued on to the village. It was 2030 hours and getting dark. Some of the patrol was still on the trail. Colonel Kling put out security all around the patrol. The headman in the village was told by an advance scout to see the Colonel in the morning.

The Colonel's tent, mess tent, and medical tent were set up one hundred yards outside of the village. The village had two wells. All the tent areas were secured, latrines were dug, and the horses were fed, washed, and brushed. The Marines ate and rested. At 1400 hours the Colonel called for the village headman. The villagers called the headman Doc. The headman Doc said he was happy to see the Marines. He said that his village has been harassed by about thirty bandits. They have taken food from them and beat up some of the village men. They have a camp three miles to the west. One of the bandits said his name was Vaco and he will be back. They have rifles, some handguns, and machetes.

Colonel Kling declared a two day rest. He said he would like twenty-five volunteers for this first skirmish. No problems. Kling said he would direct this first action. Horses, rifles, pistols, and cavalry swords, full horses Marine equipment. One hundred and eighty rounds each man. Three days rations, full canteens. Four filled water packs, shovels, ax, rope, and ammo. Three pack horses, two Navy corpsmen.
Two advance scouts were six hundred yards ahead of the patrol. Colonel Kling rode up within two hundred yards of the bandit's camp. No outer guards. Not much of a camp, about forty men and fifteen women lying around drinking and fornicating all over the area. Some of the Marines said, "I hope they leave some for us." Kling didn't want to kill the women. He said the best way to take these bandits out

161

was to charge in, shoot, and cut them down. That's just what they did. The Marines rode in killed and cut down thirty men before the bandits knew what hit them. The Marines rounded up the other ten bandits then shot them. They then rounded up the women. All the dead bodies were stacked together. The Marines were going to burn them as a warning before they left. Colonel Kling looked the other way that night. Guards were posted. Marines were around with the women. The Marines were told not to get drunk. The Marines stayed two days watching the bodies burn. The Marines then returned to the village called Mance. No casualties just some small cuts and bruises.

A village called Clego about a two days ride from Mance was having trouble with some guerrillas. The headman Doc said it was about eighteen miles north. Doc got all his information from Haitians being scared out of their villages by insurgents, guerrillas, and bandits. Kling said he was going out on this patrol. His next in command and Junior Officer said he is a Colonel and he did not have to be a leader on all the small patrols. Kling said, "Look you Boots, you would get lost if I wasn't around. Wait until you people get experience. You are playing for keeps in this game."

At a meeting two years back Colonel Kling suggested to the fledgling Army and Navy Criminal Division why not send some Junior Officers and Sergeants to study the civilian police procedures. The Marine Commandant did and it paid off. Unknown to Kling at this time the Army and Navy realized they would have a complete ring around the Panama Canal: the U.S., Cuba, Haiti, Dominican Republic, Puerto Rico, Virgin Islands, St. Croix, Leeward Islands, St. Lucia, Tobago, and Panama. The Panama Canal at this time needed much security. With the war in Europe the U.S. had to protect its protectorates. The U.S. knew two European countries would like to get a foothold in Haiti and the Dominican Republic.

Kling called for his top kick to get two messengers ready to go back to the Constabulary outside of Cape Haitien. He wrote out his message to Major Bryla to:

1) send an officer to the government offices at Cape Haitien to find out the names of the large villages and towns in the north and east

2) know population areas

3) maps, names of trouble makers, insurgents, revolutionists

4) any trustful employees or people as interpreters. We need some.

5) I will need six months supplies of everything if I am to leave Marines at these villages and towns to train police and militia.

6) send any of the Marine Junior Officers and Sergeants that had civilian police procedure training.

7) I will need one hundred mud Marines and seventy-five horse Marines 8) one doctor to travel with us and fifteen corpsmen

9) food, clothes, weapons, medical supplies

10) three machine guns 30 cal.

11) two 37mm guns - 300 rounds canister

12) one hundred 30 cal. rifles - fifty pistols- 45 cal.

13) three 60mm mortars - 60 rounds- 5 cases hand grenades

I know it will take some time before you can help us with supplies. We will also live off the land. Kling did not know the Navy had two ships, the Henderson and the Roanoke unloading Marines and supplies for the Constabulary. Major Bryla immediately sent two messengers to Colonel Kling informing him of the arrival of the ships loaded with needed supplies. He would start a supply line to Colonel Kling in three days. Four Marine Junior Officers and three Sergeants who had civilian police training were already on their way. Major Bryla said, "The Lord is with us." When the messenger gave Kling the message he said, "The Lord had heard my prayer. I will now have one hundred twenty-five horse Marines, one doctor, and seventeen corpsmen."

Chapter 25

Colonel Kling decided to hold off on the patrol to the village of Clego until he received the information he requested from Major Bryla. It was October 30th 1Mance would be called Marine Camp One. In command of the horse Marines on the trail was a Lieutenant named Sailboat Lem. Kling said, "Oh No - Not Again!" He knew Lem, a good Marine, but what a woman chaser. Lem was over leave without permission. He lived in New York. A big blonde named Mortisa Loster a female bartender was doing Lem. They got drunk and he forgot he was a Marine. Later he told his buddy that a divorcee, middle aged nurse had a hungry look in her eye when she looked at him. She wasn't bad, naive, Sailboat could never get serious. But a three way!!! Vi va French! He was named Sailboat because he liked to take his girlfriends out sailing, sailing, sailing over the ocean blue. Sailboat was lucky he never caught the French American flu. Sailboat, watch out for the French Haitian flu. When Sailboat saw Kling he almost peed in his pants. Kling was now a Colonel. Being the senior Lieutenant Sailboat knew Kling would fix him up with a good command. The village of Mance had about six hundred people in or around. For every one male there were three females. Who did Kling have in mind to leave in command of five horses and fifteen mud Marines to train police and militia forces at Mance? Kling told Sailboat about the Haitian and French Haitian women. They play for keeps. They are not naive, "bam-so long", man not here. Colonel Kling told Sailboat what he expected of him and his duty. He would be at the village of Mance for some time. He told him to be careful and not to trust anyone. Sailboat was to send a weekly report to Major Bryla by two horse Marines and they would bring available supplies and ammo back. Two Navy hospital corpsmen were attached to Sailboat's command.

November 15th 1915 all equipment, food, clothes, weapons, and medical supplies were in Mance. Colonel Kling took stock and made his plans for the patrol of Clego.

Report came in to Doc at Mance. Many bad guerrillas and bandits in the town of Clego. The information sent to Kling was that Clego was a hilly area, a town about three thousand people. Most of the people were good, honest, religious people trying to survive. Six hundred guerrillas moved in shot what government and security they had and then took over. The people raised goats, some cattle, farming, fruit, and vegetables. They also made some wine. Very little gold or money was in the town. People used the barter system. Kling said he would need for the patrol; 100 horse Marines, full equipment, 100 mud Marines, rifle, machine guns,artillery - 75 packs, mortar experience, one doctor, twelve hospital corpsmen, 6 pack mules or horses, 400 canister shot - 100 A.P. six 60mm mortars - 30mm M.S., 4- 30 cal. machine guns, 3-37mm guns, 3 cases of mill hand grenades, 5000 rounds 30 cal. ammo, 1000 rounds 45 cal. ammo, rations for ten days, feed for horses, tents, shelter, halfs, and ponchos for every Marine. Communication wires were put on and over trees and poles. Haitians cut the poles down for firewood and used the wire for building and gardens.

Twenty trustful government workers were put out to travel to Clego and tell some good people to get out of town. They then were to report back to Kling's headquarters. They were also to find out the strength, approximate number of guerrillas, weapons, and where most congregated. Kling then would put out his four Haitian scouts. When the scouts reported in on activities in the guerrilla camp Kling would send up fifty mud Marines with machine guns and 37mm guns. All guns were to be positioned. No firing. The attack would start at 0600 hours. There were six 75 pack shells to knock out buildings and 37mm guns with canister to cut down guerrillas. Some of the people could not be warned. They should know to keep down. The guerrillas had an outer guard walking aimlessly from place to place. They ran into the forward machine gun. Before the Marines could fire the guerrillas had the upper hand and shot the three Marine gunners. It was 0545 hours. Kling's 75 pack Howitzer went into action. They knocked

165

out the large building and reported positions where the guerrillas were quartered. Then they shot up some caves. The guerrillas were running and shooting at places they thought the Marines were. The 37mm guns shooting canister shot mowed them down. Marine machine gunners did a good job on them. At the end of the town the guerrillas had about eighty horses mounted and ready to charge. The machine and 37mm guns were in position. The area was hilly. Guerrillas were waving their machetes as they charged. Colonel Kling told his second in command Captain Foster to send in the hundred mud Marines after he and the horse Marines counter charged. Kling with a saber in one hand guiding his horse and a pistol charged into the guerrillas shooting and slashing. Guerrillas as well as Marines were dying. Dead horses, bodies, blood, screaming men. "Help! Help!" A Corpsman was heard. Kling's horse was shot. He fell off and broke his left arm. His top Sergeant and two horse Marines carried him to a safe position. The mud Marines came forward shooting, bayoneting guerrillas and bandits. Unfortunately, some good town people were killed. The Marines used hand grenades like baseball practice. The skirmish lasted about one and a half hours. It was a man to man fight. The Marines came out on top but the cost in casualties was high.

Casualties:
503 guerrillas and bandit dead
150 guerrillas wounded (shot) dead
300 townspeople dead
80 wounded
10 government interpreters dead
Marine Casualties
45 horse Marines dead
12 wounded - 3 Navy Corpsmen
53 mud Marines dead
15 wounded

Kling had sixty-eight horse Marines and thirty-two mud Marines left out of the two hundred twenty-five that participated in the skirmish. Some townspeople helped to bury the guerrillas and clean up the garrison. Colonel Kling would leave ten horses and twenty mud Marines to police and train a militia. One Lieutenant, two Sergeants, two Corporals, twenty-five Privates, and two trained Corpsmen. Supplies and weapons were plentiful at this time. Communications were still bad. Kling was going to the Constabulary at Cape Haitien. On the way he would stop at the village of Mance and check on Sailboat and his Marines. The dead Marines had to be buried at Clego. Walking wounded, some on horses were going to Cape Haitien. Sniping was going on by very small units of guerrillas.

Clego Camp - 30 Marines
Mance Camp - 20 Marines
Cape Haitien - approx. 125 Marines

Colonel Kling was going to Cape Haitien with a broken arm and seventy Marines. It was November 20th 1915 when Kling and his seventy Marines returned to Cape Haitien. His broken arm had been set by the one doctor they had with them at Clego. He asked Major Bryla to write out his reports. He told Bryla what events took place when he left Cape Haitien. Kling and his seventy Marines needed medical aid, food, and rest. Some of his mail from his wife caught up to him. He was happy to hear about his wife and children. His orders from the Commandant were to stay at Cape Haitien. No word was heard from Colonel Pikus or the Dominican Republic.

Chapter 26

Major Zeke was relieved from Port-au-Prince and ordered back to Quantico, Virginia to train horse Marines. Captain Eckert was there to assist him. New recruits were plentiful. Colonel Byrnes was doing an excellent job of recruiting. Colonel Pikus was having a hard time in the Dominican Republic. His unit landed two miles south of Ciudad Trujillo on September 20th 1915. The advance Marine party picked out a nice location approximately one thousand yards on the Caribbean Sea side. Fresh water was within a mile of where the new Constabulary would be located. What government the island had was no help to the small villages and towns. Outside of the capital the insurgents, bandits, and guerrillas were running wild. Pikus landed with one hundred horse Marines and one hundred fifty mud Marines, two doctors, and twenty hospital trained corpsmen. He was also promised ten Dominican French interpreters and twenty trusted government militia. All mud Marines had full equipment. Horse Marines - 45 cal. pistol,.03 rifle, cavalry sabers, horse blankets, brush, feed bag, poncho, first aid , canteens, shelter halves, lariats, saddles, bridles, 782-mess gear.

Armament- guns
6 - 30 cal. machine guns
6 - 37mm guns-canister and AP shot
4 pack 75 Howitzers -60-S
5 60mm mortars -60-S-
16 cases hand grenades
12 smoke grenades
1000 rounds 45 cal, ammo
5000 rounds 30 cal. ammo
12 picks, 12 shovels, 12 axes
2 water wagons
20 rubber water bags
25 rolls bobbed wire
lumber 2x4, 1x6, 1/2x8, nails, saws
equipment - tools to build shelter

45 lanterns

20 - barn, 10 - search lights, 5 - bullseyes, 10 - lamps

6 - 55 gal. lamp oil, 500 - wicks, 200 – candles

1000 boxes matches

300 cots

300 mosquito nets

300 - 3 gal. pails

12 cases Gi soap

300 bed linens, 600 blankets

200 hundred horses

25 mules

50 - 6 man tens, pegs

100 boxes purification papers (toilet paper)

full kitchen equipment, tent, benches

first aid and medical supplies

All of the above mentioned is some of what you paid taxes for.

Yes, "We Were Marines"! How many times did one have to come back for the same problems? This time we were staying a long time. We were building a Constabulary. Everything was going as scheduled until November 1st. The morning patrol of ten Marines did not return. After dinner Colonel Pikus called his second in command Brucie Wells to his tent. He asked what Wells had in mind. Wells said to give them twenty-four hours. The morning of November 2nd at 0930 hours a Dominican militia scout horrified Colonel Pikus, his Junior Officers, and the Sergeants standing near by. The scout reported that on the west road about two miles from the Constabulary he found ten heads. In the bush on both sides of the dirt road he found the bodies. The bodies were stripped of everything. Four of the dead had Marine Corps tattoos. All the bodies' penises had been cut off. He did not see them anywhere. He moved all the heads and bodies further in the bush and put some plant and banana leaves on them. Pikus told his second in command, all officers, and sergeants Mess Tent meeting at 1930 hours.

At the meeting Pikus told his officers that this was their

third trip to the Caribbean, Haiti, Dominican Republic, and Nicaragua. Everything should be better than it was but the situation is critical. Pikus said the fault is the political system. He said, "You Marines are going to make these people responsible for the murders and make them suffer a thousand times more. I saw torture that was unbelievable. We used to tell the recruits for not shooting marksman "ten days of molestation in a dark cell with two four hundred pound Irish girls." Kidding aside I will show no mercy for man, woman, or child responsible for these murders. We will pick up our dead and bury them." The dead were buried near the Constabulary. On November 5th 1915 two more Dominican scouts checked in. They told Colonel Pikus the people responsible for killing the Marines were at Santiago. He said about one thousand guerrillas, bandits, and hostile irregulars were making a garrison one mile outside of the town. The townspeople were living in terror. Pikus said, "We are going to go after these terrorists. We are going to have to pull something out of the bag, like more Marines. We have to leave fifty Marines at the Constabulary. Let's see now that would give us 200 Marines, 18 Dominican militia, 4 interpreters, 2 doctors, 18 corpsmen, and 18 militia. We should be so lucky! Its do or die!" Major Wells was told to call for a meeting the next day at 0930 hours for the commissioned and non commissioned officers. At 1400 hours Colonel PIkus would speak to the whole command. Pikus sent a message to Marine Command Naval Headquarters Guantanamo Bay, Cuba. He said to start the campaign he would need three hundred combat ready Marines to land at Santiago, Dominican Republic. "If can do", he will send date on landing. His command had only 200 Marines. Estimated guerrillas 1000. Haiti had no Marines to help. On November 9th word came from Guantanamo Bay "Can do". Pikus told his officers, "We should be at the town called Guayman 5 miles south of Santiago on November 26th. We will be there come hell or high water." It took four days to get combat ready. Full equipment Marines:

4 interpreters

3 machine guns - 12 Marines

3 - 37mm guns - 12 Marines

3 - 75 pack Howitzers - 12 Marines

2 - 60mm mortars - 6 Marines

Riflemen - two platoons - 100 Marines

60 horses - 5 pack - 15 pack mules

Horse Marines - 50 Marines

Communications

Transportation - ammo - 8 Marines

Equipment, food

Dominican militia - 18 armed men

to help transportation ,supplies, & ammo

Rations - 25 days

2 Doctors

18 Corpsmen - medical supplies

Pikus' message to Guantanamo, "Land combat Marines about five miles south of Santiago town called Guayman 0900 hours morning 28th November 1915." The traveling for the Pikus command was torturous with mosquitoes, fleas, bugs, heat, awful sleeping, and eating conditions. Some Marines were showing signs of malaria. Colonel Pikus said, "How could we ever lose a war with the U.S. Marines on our side?" They walked into the village of Guayman on November 25, 1915 at 1300 hours. They were five miles south of Santiago. The Marines could see one destroyer and the USS Henderson from the beach. Guards were posted. No evening mess. Oranges, bananas and hard tack were passed out. The Marines needed sleep. The sergeants were responsible for the change of guards. The O.D. Officer was over all in charge of night security. Colonel Pikus told the O.D., "Do not blow reveille until 0700 hours. Peaceful night, Thank the lord!" At 0800 hours Marines were landing from the USS Henderson. The Colonel's tent was the only tent up. Mess call, the Marines' breakfast was black coffee, soft white bread, jelly, and fried bacon. The Marines did not expect mess call. During the night the Destroyer Able's mail boat came into the beach with the soft white bread and bacon. The Marine Mess

171

Sergeant and crew went to work. Lt. Louie did not forget his Marine friends. He also sent in factory made cigarettes, pipe tobacco, and a barrel of apples. Enough for Colonel Pikus' Marines. Lt. Louie is the best scrounger the Marines have. An area was set up for the three hundred incoming Marines. All the Marines had their shelter halfs and ponchos. Mess areas were set up. Latrines were dug. Colonel Pikus called a meeting of all officers. After all the assault Marines were in their areas assignments were given out. Captain Yarotsky Platoon "A", Captain Keer Platoon "B", and Captain Walker Platoon "C". Colonel Pikus was overall in command. His command included headquarters. Total two hundred sixty. The Destroyer James added twenty trained hospital corpsmen and two doctors. Total command five hundred eighty-two. Estimated enemy one thousand. Platoon "A" and "B" will be landed four miles north of Santiago and move south against the guerilla's garrison. On signal the Destroyers James and Smith will land the Marines and standby if their four inch guns are needed. The Destroyer Able and Gunboat Doctrine will land Platoon "C" and Colonel Pikus' special platoon. The guerrilla's garrison was within range of the Destroyers Able, James, Smith, and the Gunboat Doctrine. Brucie boy was in command of the Gunboat Doctrine. Lt. Louie was in command of the Flotilla.

The Flotilla saturated the guerrilla's garrison, the center of it, east, south, north, and west with shrapnel, AP, and common missile (shell) fire from their minor caliber 4 inch guns. Could there be any people left alive? "You could bet your life there were." Hiding in holes and caves. Fifty horse Marines rode forward guarding the machine and 37mm guns. The 37mm guns raked the areas with canister shot. Colonel Pikus gave the signal. Three hundred blood thirsty Marines yelled "off with their heads". The Marines shot, bayoneted, and used their rifle butts on any males they found in holes or caves. Marines were also killed. The horse Marines shot and cut down the guerrillas who were trying to run away. The Gunship Monroe landed one hundred fifty trusted militia

Marine trained soldiers on the dock outside of Santiago. Their job was to clean out Santiago of bandits and guerrilla hideouts. A Constabulary of fifty-five U.S. Marines and one hundred Dominican militia was established. They would travel to the small villages and towns to drive out the bandits. Major Wills would be temporarily in charge.

The skirmish (campaign) on the guerrilla garrison and thereabouts was over. It was December 13th 1915.

Casualties:

60 Marine - dead

70 Marine - wounded

4 Hospital Corpsmen Navy - dead

1 Doctor Navy - dead

6 Dominican Militia - dead

2 Sailors crewmen accident on the Monroe - dead

Colonel Pikus buried the dead Marines near the new Constabulary. Sixty-five Marines and four Navy corpsmen were to stay with the militia at the new Constabulary. The United States established a Military Government for the Dominican Republic. Colonel Pikus received orders to reinforce the Constabularies of Cape Haitien, Port-au-Prince in Haiti, and Ciudad Trujillo on the west coast of the Dominican Republic with fifty Marines in each area. The rest of the survivors of the Dominican Republic campaign two hundred and four Marine, Militia, and Corpsmen will set up a Constabulary at Jeremie, a coastal town on the west coast of Haiti.

West Indies

Marine Caribbean Commanders

Constabulary

Haiti

Cape Haitien - Major Stanley Bryla

Port-au-Prince - Kerr

Jeremie - Captain Walker

Dominican Republic

Santiago - Captain Yarotsky

Ciudad Trujillo - Captain Johnson

The Destroyers Able and James will help with the transfer. All ILRP Officers, furlough Marines, end of enlistment, and medical problem Marines will leave from Port-au-Prince on December 19th 1915 on the USS Henderson at 1100 hours for Norfolk, Virginia. The Henderson is expected to dock at Norfolk on December 23rd. Some may be home for Christmas!

Chapter 27

Eleven hundred hours on December 23, 1915 the USS Henderson docked at pier 7 Norfolk, Virginia. Gathering all their luggage and saying, "Thank you and farewell" to the Captain of the Henderson the six ILRP Officers departed from the ship. They immediately requested transportation to the Marine barracks from the Harbor Master's office. They checked in at the Marine Commander's office. It was relayed to the ILRP office in Washington, D.C. The Duty Sergeant's return message was, "Pick up M.B. Nor., F. 23 H.Hr, to ILRP Headquarters Dec. 23, 1915."

Fourteen hundred hours the six officers decided to do some Christmas shopping at Stacey's Department store. Colonel Kling was having trouble with his broken left arm. Pikus said, "What the hell, did you forget how to ride a horse?" Kling answered back, "Not a dead one." Ed Pikus helped his shipmate Kling to do some Christmas shopping. All the Officers returned to the Marine barracks. They left their purchases with their luggage. The Marine O.D. Officer accompanied them to the Naval Officer's Mess where they had a steak dinner, and then they went to the Officer's Club for a couple of drinks. Twenty two hundred hours they returned to the Marine Barracks. Twenty three thirty hours they were on their way to the ILRP Headquarters. The Navy provided two command vehicles. They arrived at ILRP at 0630 hours December 24th. They all hit the sack. At 1130 hours General Dell Rico called the ILRP Headquarters and he told the Duty Sergeant to wake up the officers at 1200 hours. They must be in uniform and have their written reports completed at fifteen hundred hours.

The meeting started with roll call then turning in their reports.

   Colonel Walter Kling
   Colonel Edward Pikus
   Major Robert Zeke
   Major John Wells

Captain Frank Eckert

Captain Charles Sambach

General Dell Rico started to speak and in walked the Commandant of the Marine Corps. General John Smith. The General embraced each officer and said, "My sons!" He said to Colonel Kling, "I heard you had trouble sitting on a horse." Kling said, "General, the horse I was sitting on had fourteen bullet holes in him before he went down throwing me off. He didn't know I was a Colonel." General Smith wished all the officers a Merry Christmas and Happy New Year and then departed.

General Dell Rico said, "Now for your next assignments. Two weeks (14 days) furlough from December 25, 1915 to January 8, 1916 for Colonel Pikus, Majors Zeke and Wells, and Captains Eckert and Sambach. January 8th, 9th, 10th, and 11th you officers will report to Captain Dr. Russo Quantico Hospital Virginia for three day evaluation of your wounds from previous campaigns, and present health and fitness exams. You will then return to ILRP Headquarters on January 12th for the results of your examinations. Colonel Kling you are on leave from the evening of December 24 until December 27. You will report to Quantico Hospital to see Dr. Russo on the 28th at 1300 hours for examination of your left arm in cast also, your medical and fitness exam. You will then report to ILRP Headquarters for you thirty days medical leave papers December 29, 1915 until January 30, 1916.

General Dell Rico telephoned the Duty Sergeant at ILRP Headquarters on January 13, 1916 to inform the five ILRP Officers that a meeting was scheduled for January 15, 1916 at 0900 hours at ILRP Headquarters. Full dress uniforms. The Commandant may drop in. As usual General Dell Rico was fifteen minutes late. The officers passed the time talking about their Christmas leaves. General Dell Rico said, "Sorry Gentlemen, I was held up by an accident on the road." Lieutenant Louie Byrnes patrols in the South Atlantic and Caribbean has reported cases of piracy. Lt. Byrnes has a lot of ocean to patrol with only three destroyers. Now, with the war on in Europe interventionists are still trying to acquire a foot hold on some islands in the Caribbean and cause problems for the United States. German ships have been sighted off the island of Antigua, a British possession. England and the Germans are fighting. What are German ships doing cruising off the islands? The British have many possessions with little or no Navy in the area. Lt. Byrnes has the Caribbean Sea to patrol and the water ways to and around the Panama Canal. We should not forget when we were building the canal that two European countries were giving us trouble. General Dell Rico said, "The Commandant said that my five ILRP Officers know how to clean this piracy racket. They did it before."

Colonel Pikus will be in command. Majors Wells, Zeke, Captains Eckert and Sambach with ten ranking Marines will accompany Colonel Pikus. Full equipment. Colonel Pikus knows what to bring. Transportation to Norfolk, Va. then to Marine barracks in San Juan, Puerto Rico. Captain Cross and Chief Petty Officer Bruce Jones will be waiting for you people. Jones has the Gunboat Doctrine and is ready for action. One 75-mm Howitzer on the stern and a two pounder on the bow. Two 60-mm mortars and six 30 cal. machine guns also, small arms, ammunition, and hand grenades.

Colonel Pikus and his fourteen Marines boarded the Doctrine. The crew of the Doctrine numbered twelve including Cross and Jones. Twenty-seven seasoned Veterans looking for a fight. Captain Cross said, "Steaks and beer for tonight. Tomorrow trim the ship. The next day we sail, February 1, 1916." Cross said Chief Petty Officer Bruce Jones would be the Captain of the Gunboat Doctrine on this trip. Lieutenant Louie Byrnes telegraphed Captain Cross the day before sailing. Byrnes said the information he had was that the so called pirates were operating out of an island named Larbuda, a British possession. The British should be notified of our action. Captain Cross notified the British Consul. With help from the U.S. Naval Command, Washington, D.C. he received permission from the British saying, "Go! Go! Go! Clean it up!" Captain Bruce stopped at St. Croix one of the

U.S.'s possessions for any information on the piracy. Captain Bruce had permission to stop for fuel at St. Kitter, a British possession. Captain Bruce picked up all the information that was needed to clear the area of pirates. It was all agreed a German Naval Officer by the name of Karl Von Hinenburg was causing the so called piracy around the British ships and possessions. Germany was at war with England. Von Hinenburg was causing trouble on the ships and British islands it appears and no doubt the German Army and Navy Logistics were wrong. England had no troops or ships to take away from the war in Europe to protect their possessions in the Caribbean. England's friend and later ally the United States would and could handle the so-called pirates.

Information from the radio room of the Doctrine said that the twelve hundred people living on Larbuda claimed no country owned them. They were independent. The French gave them independence in the year 1850. The French said the island was not worth keeping. No value, only an expense. The fishing and growing crops were not good. However, the people living there survived. They lived off farming, fishing, and making rum. Von Hinenberg was permitted to dock his special built ocean boats for a price. The people did not know what he was up to. Von Hinenberg would take his boats out, shell a British ship by firing his boat's two pounders and machine guns. He would take what he could use from the ships he stopped and would damage the ships as much as he could. Von Hinenberg took over the island of Larbuda. He gave the people what he stole from the ships and islands he looted. His command of thirty sailors were all well trained in boating, gunnery, and killing for their European leader.

Colonel Pikus called the twenty-seven Marines and sailors together for a meeting after leaving St. Kitter Island. Maps were laid out so all could see. It was February 13, 1916. Pikus said, "We will attack when we get Von Hinenberg's boats in port. He would murder us on the water. The island is one mile by two miles long. There are two small villages, one on the north coast and one on the south coast. Very few people live in the villages. Von Hinenberg docks one boat on the north and one on the south coast, smart German. The morning of February 16th Major Wells, Captain Eckert, and six Marines at 0400 hours will land from a small boat near the docked German boat. If the boat is out they will have to hide out until it comes in. The information we have is that the boats are out no longer than twelve hours. It will take us two hours to reach the boat docked at the north pier. If the German boat is in Major Wells will give us two hours before he destroys the boat and "Deep Sixes" the German crew and their land quarters. Remember, no prisoners." Colonel Pikus would stand by with six sailors armed if support was needed. Captain Bruce would be on deck with guns ready.

Colonel Pikus and his Marines did an extremely good job of destroying Von Hinenberg's boats and crew. Karl Von Hinenberg did not escape. Major Zeke shot him in the head. After the cleaning up and destruction of Von Hinenberg's "not useable" guns, ammo, equipment, and supplies Colonel Pikus told his Marines to round up all the inhabitants, first the north town then they would sail down to the south town. Colonel Pikus told the inhabitants not to rent out any land or property. "First speak to the agent of the U.K. or the U.S. government."

Casualties:
30 suspected German Navy Men
Captain Karl Von Hinenberg

U.S. Casualties
2 U.S. Marines (1 shot in the arm, 1 shot in the leg)
That was the end of piracy in 1916. The Gunship Doctrine went back to Puerto Rico. The Destroyer Chase took fifteen Marines back to Norfolk, Virginia. Two Marines were hospitalized at the Naval Hospital at San Juan, Puerto Rico.

Chapter 28

ILRP Headquarters, Washington, DC. February 28, 1916 - all ILRP Officers including Colonel Kling were writing their activity reports for the past three months. The Commandant was very concerned about his special ILRP Officers. Colonel Kling's arm healed well and he passed the Fitness Report for Duty. General Dell Rico telephoned Colonel Kling to set up a meeting for March 1, 1916 at 0900 hours at ILRP Headquarters. "Yes, you could bet on it." General Dell Rico was fifteen minutes late again. "Traffic was heavy," he said. Captain Eckert said laughing, "Sometimes a horse is faster." General Dell Rico said, "I know a Marine who needs a Nicaraguan vacation for a year. Ha, Ha, Ha!" Everyone was laughing.

"Gentlemen, you must volunteer for this assignment. Colonels Pikus and Kling, I believe still have their Revolutionary bad guy passes." The chopa seal clearance. Sometimes it pays to be in the know. We have trouble along the border between the U.S. and Mexico. The United States is going to send down General Mershing with the 10th and 12th Cavalry. With the war in Europe I can see why the belligerent countries fighting France and England are giving the United States problems. The enemies of France and England know the U.S. is supporting them. You Marines are going under cover to Vera Cruz, Tampico, and Mexico City to obtain definite first hand information if foreign interventionists are responsible for the border incidents.

The people that live near the border on the American side are being raided for guns, money, and food. People are also being shot. The U.S. wants first hand information:
1. Are the Bandits and Revolutionists working together and for whom?
2. Who is supplying money and guns to them?
3. Names of politicians who have large estates for the border raids.
4. Mexican, American, and foreign corporates of companies and corporations in oil wells, gold, silver, and

copper mines.

You people have been through situations like this before. You all speak Mexican-Spanish better than the Mexicans. You know how to look, dress, and conduct yourselves. Remember, "Take nothing that can identify you as an American." You could get killed or tortured to death. You do not have to volunteer. All six ILRP Officers volunteered.

Colonel Pikus, Major Wells, Captain Sambach "Unit 1", Colonel Kling, Major Zeke, Captain Eckert "Unit 2" - You are all American renegades, banditos. Your command post, Pinar del Rio, Cuba and Laredo, Texas. Telephone and telegraph code -ROT- Return - Code - TEM. Unit 1 will work its way by trade boats from Miami, Florida to Havana then to Tampico, Mexico. Unit 2 by the same route. Use different trade boats to Vera Cruz. Both units must memorize our agents' locations for horses, guns, and equipment. Our agents in Mexico are good hard working Mexicans who want the help of the United States to straighten out their country. Our Mexican agents have to be careful they cannot get around like you people. They are always under some kind of surveillance because of their government jobs.

General Dell Rico said, "I believe you people will get the information." The agents you contact may help get out information to your command post. Fourteen days is the limit for your investigation. Both units then will travel to the town of Pachuca outside of Mexico City. Getting the desired information from the government offices by Mexican employees most times is extremely difficult. You may have to bribe and hurt people. Be careful, you may have to travel around the country side for information. Sometimes the inhabitants know what's going on. One week in and around Mexico City then go to pier six, slip eight, Vera Cruz Inlet. A Captain Viera will be waiting for you on the sailboat "Blackhawk". He will take you people by boat up to Brownsville, Texas. Go to Laredo, turn in your reports - and then stand by.

March 31, 1916 - Laredo Command Post, Texas communication - D5 - D.C. - COM. - M.C. to Colonel W. Kling.

181

Travel border from Laredo west to Cludda Juarez. Destroy any bandit known hideouts that the Army missed. Eagle Pass and Pielaro Negras are reported dangerous locations. Laredo Command will supply needed equipment, guns, and horses. Colonels Pikus and Kling asked for fifty Marines, fifty-two horses, ten pack mules, one 30 cal. machine gun, ammo, and one hundred fifty hand grenades also, two Navy Medical Corpsmen and three Mexican interpreters. All sixty-one men in the patrol will dress like the Mexican peasantry men, not shaven, short beard, and mustached. Let hair grow. Let horse and body odors stay around. Wear sombreros, blue or red neckerchief, and blue bands around sombreros for identification. No loud talking in English.

Weapons are always a problem. Use 1903 .30 cal. Springfield rifles and Model 94 Winchester 30-30 lever action carbines. Make sure ammo supply is sufficient. Supplies and ammo will be at check points.

The United States was close to war. Border guards could not handle the job. The United States did not have enough Army troops to run all over fifteen hundred miles of border. The Army was training for war. This in-between job had the right men, the ILRP Marine Unit. Five miles before Eagle Pass, Colonel Pikus, Major Wells, two Marine Corporals, and one interpreter went forward to scout out the pass. Sure as hell's a fire, before the outer brim of the pass had about one hundred, what appeared to be brigand eating, sleeping, and grab assing. What made the scouts sure they were bandits, they had two men and a woman stretched out on crosses. No clothes on them and they were bleeding. Two of the bandits were fornicating with two young females and slapping them. Local people said they were bandits. Colonel Pikus said to Kling, "Walt, we are going to "Deep Six" all of them." Kling said about 0400 hours tomorrow morning, twenty Marines, who are on their way now will quietly move up to hand grenade throwing distance. They will each throw three grenades on the awake and sleeping bandits. They will then back off, return to their horses, and stand by as a reserve unit.

Colonel Kling will charge the bandits on the outer brim with sabers drawn, cut and shoot what they see on the brim, then go through the pass and "Deep Six" bandits on the inner brim. The twenty reserve Marines with sabers and pistols will "Deep Six" what bandits they see alive on the outer brim. They then will help the Marines on the inner brim. Some of the bandits escaped.

Casualties:
2 Marines dead
6 Marines wounded

Bandit Casualties
65 dead
20 wounded - all shot
4 women dead

After the clean up Kling told Captains Eckert and Sambach to take twenty-three Marines to clean up the next stop, the village of Del Rio. The rest of the unit will catch up. Kling said, "We have to dispatch the wounded and dead Marines to the nearest Army check point."

Waiting for the Army unit from La Pryor to pick up Kling's dead and wounded Marines three bandits were discovered hiding in the brush. They said they were good bandits. Did not kill anyone. Kling said, "I have just the place for good bandits." He hung one on each side of the pass. The third bandit he branded on each cheek of his behind (ass) with the Marine "M" then he let him go, as a warning to other bandits. The U.S. Army Department reconsidered its position on troops looking for bandits on the border of Texas and Mexico. The U.S. Army will cross over the boarder to the Mexican side in pursuit. One company of the 10th Cavalry, two hundred strong will zig-zag a path from Big Band National Park, Boquillas, Texas supported by four companies of cavalry to El Paso. Kling said, "Thank God the Army woke up to how important border control is." The Army transferred six privates to replace Kling's casualties. Kling had sixty-one men again in his command. Del Rio was no problem for Captains

Eckert and Sanbach. They captured fifteen live bandits after a brief fight. Eckert hung two, and then shot thirteen with his firing squad. Eckert then declared a two day rest. Horse, clothes, and body washing. Captain Sambach checked the Marines' rifles, ammo, and safe places for the horses to feed. It was April 15, 1916 before Kling's command arrived at Del Rio.

Kling held a meeting to tell his officers the Army was taking over at Boquillas, Texas. Kling's command would check out the border towns of Shumia and Langtry. The traveling he said would be rough. They would clean out villages for three hundred miles. Supplies would be picked up at Langtry, Texas. Kling believed he would not have any trouble until he reached Boquillas, Texas. He was right. A few bad guys here and there, a couple of hangings and the areas covered were secured. The ILRP Unit had four casualties, two dead and two wounded Marines. May 5, 1916 Kling's unit was on the outskirts of Boquillas. Gunfire was heard. A scout reported to Colonel Kling the 10th Cavalry was engaged in a skirmish with what the Army believed was approximately two hundred Mexican bandits and revolutionists. Major Katsenberger was in command of the cavalry. Colonels Kling and Pikus, seniors in Command, would take over. Major Katsenberger said, "What are your orders Colonels?" Kling said to Pikus, "Ed, we usually work one command." Ed Pikus said, "K" comes before "P" so take over. They both started laughing. Kling told Major Zeke and his second in command to take fifty Army Troopers down the Rio Grande River about one mile east, cross over to the Mexican side and to come up in back of Boquillas, Mexico. He would be on the left flank to center, deploy his men and cut a good field of fire for his machine gun. Wait for the signal, two red flares. Put Army officers in charge of their men. Major Wells was to go up river and cross over. He would be right flank to center in back of Boquillas with Army officers and forty troopers. All officers and non com looked over the maps. Captan Sambach and an Army officer will also cover the left flank with forty troopers. Colonels Kling and Pikus will advance with forty-five Marines and forty-six troopers with sabers and pistols out charging the Mexican bandits and revolutionists. Most of the Mexican bandits seem sure of themselves by not seeking protection. They were out there with their machetes and swords swinging.

"What a charge !" The Marines, Army troopers, and bandits slashing. The bandits moved back to the Rio Grande River crossing it and that was the name of the game. Zeke and Wells slaughtered them. Colonels Kling and Pikus, twenty Army troopers, and ten Marines had cuts on their bodies - some very serious.

Casualties:

50 Army Troopers dead

25 Troopers wounded

10 Marines dead

15 Marines wounded

3 Army Officers dead

On the United States side of Boquillas a telegram waited for Colonels Kling and Pikus. "Well Done" report to Quantico, Virginia with unit by horse, rail, or whatever way available. CS-MA-Wash.,D.C. Before Colonel Kling's unit left for Quantico, Virginia the six Army soldiers who were replaced asked Colonel Pikus if they could transfer to the Marine Corp. Colonel Pikus said to Kling, "What do you think Walt?" Kling said they should be Marines. They fought like Marines and did save some wounded Marines' lives. They go with us. We will get them transferred if they can pass an ILRP test and do three months in our training program we can use them. We need some replacements.

Chapter 29

June 5, 1916 - Quantico, Virginia, Colonel Kling's command less two Navy Corpsmen and three Mexican interpreters total forty-one. Marines were put in isolation in "H" Barracks Training Co. The fifteen severely wounded Marines had to be left at an Army hospital three miles north of Boquillas, Texas. After one week of medical examinations, ten Marines had to stay at the Quantico hospital for restitching. Some were given furloughs. All the ILRP Officers were told to report to their headquarters at Installation and Logistics 545 Independence Road Washington, D.C. As the officers arrived at their headquarters they were given a seven day leave. They were to report back June 28th for a meeting at 1300 hours.

Betty and Ann were so happy to have their husbands home. Pikus' son was twelve years old and his daughter eleven. Colonel Kling's son was eleven and his daughter ten. Past birthdays were celebrated. Betty and Ann had a swimming pool ten feet by twenty feet constructed with two little bath houses in the rear of their properties. They were teaching nursing at the hospital. The hospital had a program for females ages seventeen to twenty-five, not married with at least two years of public or private high school. Physical and mental testing was required. It was a three years training course. Schooling four days weekly 9:00 am to 4:30 pm daily. Requirment: to work sixteen hours as an assistant to floor nurses or outpatient treatment. The students shall eat, sleep, and clean the nursing home. No boyfriends visiting! Parents can only take their student out on their day off. Physicals, background checks, and signing agreements were part of the program. First class nurses' salary one hundred dollars. Students received ten dollars monthly. Ann told Pikus she had a student that was a terror. Her name was Elaine. She would sneak out after curfew and hang out with a motley gang at the city public pool. I heard she gets drunk sometimes. Elaine is in my class and I am responsible for her during training. Ed, is there such a thing as a lock chastity belt? Could the belts be a requirement for some girls? How could one distinguish? Ed Pikus told Ann to tell Walt about her problem. He will throw a good scare into your student Elaine. I remember a problem like that when Walt and I were stationed at Manzanill, Cuba. Boy, did Walt straighten out the nurses at the Manzanill Hospital. All the girls liked Walt. He tells it straight from the mouth and heart. When Walt and I were nurse lovers we always had a good time. The nurses hated to see us leave. Colonels Kling and PIkus needed the seven day leave. Their corps and country would never give them the credit due. Their families showered them with love.

ILRP Headquarters, Washington, D.C. June 28, 1916 1300 hours General Dell Rico called the meeting that was scheduled to order. Present at the meeting were:

Colonel Kling
Colonel Pikus
Major Zeke
Major Wells
Captain Eckert
Captain Sambach
Commander F. Kling USCG
Lieutenant L. Byrnes USN

General Dell Rico said he was very happy to see his fellow officers. He said we had come a long way together. Colonel Byrnes was unable to attend the meeting. He was on the West Coast recruiting. Commander Frank Kling and Lt. Louie Byrnes had been relieved of their present duties. "Gentlemen," General Dell Rico said, "you people no doubt are up on the war news in Europe. I believe we will be in it next year. Our country has a big problem on the borders of foreign ports." Shipping of guns and drugs on the East Coast. Federal, state, and local law enforcement officers are being overwhelmed with narcotic arrests. The selling of the drugs, cannabis, marijuana, hashish, and opium can be purchased all over the city of New York. First I need six volunteers. Thank you gentlemen for volunteering for the East Coast assignment: Colonel Walter F. Kling, Major Robert Zeke, Captain Frank

Eckert, and Commander Frank Kling. You four gentlemen will start growing short beards and mustaches. You will dress as longshore men, rugged in character, sometimes unpleasant and disagreeable. You will all have jobs on a tramp banana boat. Commander F. Kling will be your Captain. The Grande Panama Company is leasing a boat to the United States and the company is happy repairs will be made on the boat. The company was going to junk the boat. Very few people know about this assignment. This boat is called "Yo Misno". It is a small island to island tramp steam boat. Seven Navy men will operate the boat. Six Marines and you people will do the destruction work. You will have machine guns, rifles, hand guns, grenades, oil, dynamite, and other flammable materials.

Gentlemen this assignment may take eight months. It will start July 15, 1916. Your boat will make the following stops: Hoboken, New Jersey to La Ceiba Honduras, Bluefields Nicaragua, Puerto Limon, Costa Rica, and Panama. Hoboken will be home port. Your trips will be Panama to Boston with bananas. Miami, Florida to Costa Rica, wherever banana and tropical fruits can be picked up in Central or South America for export. Suspected countries in drug farming, laboratories, and drug distribution are Mexico, Bolivia, Venezuela, Columbia, Nicaragua, and Panama. One way you can work it is when you get to a port like Puerto Limon on the East Coast of Costa Rica, the Marine guards will enforce unauthorized people to stay off the boat. You rough looking ILRP Marines, Stevedores by now will look like you could use a drink, bath, and women. Start hanging out in the local gin mills and bars. Find out where the farms of poppies and cannabis are located. Take your time. Captain Kling can always find boat trouble to stay in port longer. You people get out and find, burn, and destroy cannabis and poppy fields and farms. You people have the license to take life (kill). Be careful. If you pick up information make sure it is right. Give it to our agents who will be waiting at U.S. Ports.

The ILRP Stevedores' stop at Joe's Wonder Bar on Water St.

in Puerto Limon they hit pay dirt. The first male person they met at the bar was selling marijuana cigarettes. His name was Oscar. They bought cigarettes and started drinking rum. They got Oscar drunk. He told them where he saw poppies and cannabis growing. It was about two miles outside of town in a banana tree forest. The ILRP Marine Stevedores stole some horses and after two hours of searching they found the farm and fields. At 2400 hours they spread oil and flammables around. Fires were set. Unfortunately, two male persons believed to be guards were deep sixed. Some of the fields were dry and burnt quickly.

They returned to their boat. Commander Frank Kling told the town of Puerto Limon authorities no crew members were off the boat. The Puerto Limon Police were looking for saboteurs and murderers. Commander Kling loaded his boat with bananas then took off for Hoboken, New Jersey. Kling gave his crew two days leave. It was August 13, 1916. The boat was loaded with some farm machines and tools.

On August 18th they were on their way to San Juan, Nicaragua for bananas and melons. August 24th found the ILRP Marine Stevedores drinking rum at Querero Bar two city blocks away from the dock. What a place! The marijuana smoke was so bad they could hardly see. Three females approaching were not good looking. They asked if Kling and the Stevedores were interested in a night of love. Kling, Pikus, and Eckert felt sorry for these women. They knew how tough it was for a girl to make a living down here but, as the new culture expression goes "What Malo Mujers". Their names were Louisa, Teresa, and Anna. Kling gave them two dollars each and told them to shove off. One thing this unit did not want was to go home with was a Caribbean disease. Pikus said his wife said many good nurses with hot pants ruined their careers going around with switchers, Caribbean style.

Chapter 30

The ILRP Marines did not find any poppies or cannabis growing in or within ten miles of San Juan, Nicaragua. Very few drug merchants were located. The "Yo Misno" was loaded with bananas and melons. The next stop was Boston, Massachusetts, U.S.A. It was September 14, 1916 bananas and melons were unloaded at pier 1 in Boston. The boat was loaded with pipe and drilling equipment for Caracas, Venezuela. They left Boston on September 18, 1916 and arrived in Caracas on September 30th. A Venezuelan agent working for the United States Government met the boat. After proper identification, the agent said that a plantation farm was eight miles outside of Maracry and not only grew plantains but cannabis and poppies. It was also a drug prep and distribution center. The farm was approximately eighteen miles from the dock. If they were lucky and destroyed the center they would have to return to the boat by water from Port Cabello. One of Comento's men would be able to do the job of destruction.

October 2, 1916 Colonel Kling, Major Zeke, and Captain Eckert joined Comento and three of his men on his plantation farm one mile outside of Caracas. Comento had eight horses, cans of oil, dynamite, and a plant killer called Pequeno Polilla Veneno (little moth poison). Each one of his men had a rifle, pistol, knife, and ammunition. Kling's men had one dozen fragmentation and incinerating grenades, also rifles and pistols. Comento said the drug plant had three guards outside twenty-four hours a day. He knew their usual areas of patrolling. The drug plant guards were out approximately one quarter of a mile away from the plant. Colonel Kling told Major Zeke to take one of Comento's men and "Deep Six" the crossroad guard. Eckert and one of Comento's men will "Deep Six" the north approach wagon road guard. Kling, Comento, and two of his men will take the direct approach to the cannabis fields and start burning. They will then attack the distribution center throwing fragmentation and incinerating grenades. After the outer guards are "Deep Sixed" you four men will be our reserve to shoot down any opposition. No one is to be left alive. Jufero, Comento's top man was knifed in the stomach to heart and died without a sound. The guard heard his approach. Zeke got behind the guard and cut his throat. Grenades were thrown at the front and back entrance of the distribution building. Men and women started pouring out and were shot down. "You live with the devil, you die with the devil." Many people were dying. The destruction was complete. Think of all the destruction these people caused in the world with their opium and marijuana. The horses were all together. This gave them a good start to reach the boat at Puerto Cabello. They met a two man outer horse patrol that came to see what was going on. These men were shot and killed before they knew what hit them. The six of them; Kling, Zeke, Eckert, Comento, his two men, Juan and Mozo made the small boat. They were transferred to the steamboat "Yo Misno".

Comento, Juan, and Mozo were known around La Guaira Port and Caracas, Venezuela. Comento was an exporter of plantains. Juan and Muzo worked his farm and helped with packing and sales. They were not suspects on the drug farm raid. The raid helped Comento's business. It knocked out a competitor. Captain Kling's only allegiance at this time was the care of the Grande Panama Company steam boat "Yo Misno". The decrepit boat received a half ass overhauling. The boat was doing the job.

The next country on the drug list was Columbia. Luck was with Captain Kling. He was approached by a Venezuelan exporter who could have a sale if his minerals could be shipped to the ports of Cartagena and Buenaventura, Columbia. Bauxite and aluminum were the shipment. They would have to go through the Panama Canal to get to Port Buenaventura, Columbia.

On October 10, 1916 the boat was loaded with bauxite and aluminum. Containers were used. Cartagena, Columbia was located on the northwest corner of Columbia. This port was high on the drug list. Pto-Berrs on the Magdalena River area grew cannabis and poppies. The drug laboratory and distribution centers were located at Monterrta and Suqaamosa. The drug leaders who hit men and guards were from the tough ranks of the military and discharged police officers corps. These people would just blow you away. Mayhem and murder was their specialty. Colonel Kling asked if Colonel Pikus, Major Wells, and Captain Sambach could join them. Washington telegraphed back "can do". The Destroyer James would meet them fifteen miles off the coast of Cartagena on October 16th (that's nautical miles).

The steamboat "Yo Misno" was loaded and ready to sail out of Port LaGuairo, Venezuela on October 11th. The steamboat would wait 15 miles off the coast of Cartagena, Columbia for the Destroyer James. The Destroyer James arrived on October 19th. The ILRP Officers were all together and happy to see each other. Twelve special combat Marines and two Navy corpsmen were attached. Colonel Kling now had twenty people in his unit. A reserve unit on the "Yo Misno" would be Commander Kling's seven Navy men and six Marines. This job was to destroy all farms, fields, distribution, laboratory, and transportation systems of drugs from Columbia to the United States. The operation would start at Cartagena then Cuoina, Bucaramaza, and Plo Cerrio, Columbia. Next stop the Canal Zone for food, fuel, supplies, and information. Bogeta, Villavica, Buena Ventura, and Colamaro, Columbia will be the last investigations. The USS James brought some of the weapons, ammunition, and food to hold them until they reached the Panama Canal Zone.

When all hands were on the steamboat maps, equipment, and field food were issued. The unit received instructions on each Marine's part. The final plans were made. The steamship docked at Port Cartagena on October 22, 1916. The Marines would receive help in Columbia from the Oscar Viera family. Oscar Viera was a U.S. Marine in Sgt. Kling's unit on February 18, 1898 he was killed while on a secret mission. Sgt. Kling made sure the Viera family in Columbia received all of Oscar's money, belongings, and whatever he was entitled to.

Oscar Viera Senior left Colombia in 1896. A relative helped him get into the United States. He picked up enough English in a year to get into the Marines. His son in Columbia was four years old. Oscar Sr. was told if he stayed in the Marines for five years he would become an American citizen. Some strings must have been pulled to get him into the Marines. Enlistments were down in 1896. Oscar Sr. wanted to get his family to the United States. The Spanish-American War had started. He was shot by a sniper and died. Oscar Viera Junior lived twenty miles outside of Cartagena, Columbia. The Viera family; three brothers and two sisters were American agents. They owned a cement factory, coffee, and cocoa bean export business. Information to and from the United States came through the export business. Cannabis and poppy fields grew in the Coina and Bucarmaza areas not far from the Magdalena River. Colonel Kling and his twenty Marine unit met with Oscar Viera Jr. on the steamship "Yo Misno" that was docked at Cartagena. Oscar Viera hired Captain Frank Kling to take a shipment of cocoa beans and coffee to the Canal Zone after the cannabis and poppy fields were destroyed. Oscar said that eight men could do the job. "Deep Six" the four night guards and inflame the fields of cannabis and poppy flowers and spread the flammable chemicals around. Use hand grenades and dynamite sticks to fire and destroy the laboratory and distribution houses. Oscar had two trusted friends. Kling said he would take Wells, Zeke, Eckert and six MP Marines. It was October 24, 1916. At twenty-four hundred hours Wells, Zeke, and Oscar's two men "Deep Sixed" the four guards. They spread flammable chemicals and started fires. Kling and three MP Marines threw grenades through the windows of the laboratory and an outer house. Four males came out of the labs and were shot dead. Cutting the screen windows had been no problem. Two males came out of the outer house and they were shot. Eckert and three MP Marines dynamited and threw grenades into the distribution house. Eight males came running out. All were shot. Oscar Jr. and his two men by horseback returned to their homes. Kling, Zeke, Wells,

Eckert, and the six MP Marines returned to the boat two men at a time. There were no casualties. The boat was already loaded. It sailed out with the tide to the Panama Canal Zone. Bells, sirens, and shots could be heard coming from Cartagena. The raiding and burning fields were in the Bucaramaza area. Oscar Jr. said he would take care and destroy the fields in Cuoina.

Chapter 31

The steamship "Yo Misno" was berthed outside of Colon, Panama on October 29th 1916. The U. S. Government agents from the Agriculture Department were waiting to see Colonel Kling. They wanted a report on growing poppies and cannabis in cornfields and vegetable gardens. Also, what chemicals were used to destroy the opium poppy. After proper identification and correct code words Kling gave them the information they wanted. In Colon Captain Kling and half of his crew went out to scrounge the supplies they needed from the Government warehouses without the red tape and signing for everything. Colonel Peterson of the U. S. Army Provost Marshal Office was looking for the boat "Yo Misno", he had been informed by the Chief of the Army Operation H.Q., Washington that the "Yo Misno" tramp steamboat was expected to berth at Colon on or about October 29th or 30th. Colonel Peterson went to the Harbor Master's Office to find out where the "Yo Misno" was berthed. Peterson found the boat. He sounded off, "May I come aboard?" Colonel Kling heard him and told him to come aboard. Peterson identified himself and gave the day code word. Colonel Peterson said he was the Provost Marshal and that he had lost two investigators and a lieutenant investigating drugs around the town of Colon and Army section of the Canal Zone. He said he believed the Navy was also having a problem. Peterson said the local police and law in Panama City, LaPalma, and Colon were not much help. There was one detective by the name of Juan Torrio in Panama City who could be trusted. Kling said he was informed by the "Yo Misno" radio operator about a message in code. The message was to help Colonel Peterson Provost Marshall, Canal Zone G.S. USMC - ILRP - 1342-Priority I-G.D.R. Colonel Kling called for a meeting onboard after evening mess. All the ILRP Officers saw Colonel Peterson leave the boat. The subject was open for discussion. Colonel Pikus said let us check out the city and Port of Colon, Panama City, and Balboa. They are the suspected areas of export. Commander Kling also received orders from the Navy to assist Colonels Kling and Pikus. Kling asked Peterson to contact Detective Juan Torrio. He wanted all the information on companies in Colon that exported to the United States. Detective Torrio said he could get leave and would meet Colonel Kling at the Army Provosts' Marshall Office on November 3, 1916 at 1100 hours. While waiting for Detective Torrio Colonel Pikus said, "Let's split in two's and check out the bars, dens of activity, and whorehouses. Keep your mind on our work. Act the part, but do not participate. Nada!" Kling and Zeke checked out the bars on Pearl Street and whorehouses on River Road. They got some action and a lead on the name of Baraja. He was a card dealer in the Menta Bar. The Menta Bar was a hang out for military personnel. It was the amusement bar of the Canal Zone. You could play all kinds of card games, be served exotic drinks, and have sex in ways you never heard about. Gonorrhea was passed around like a badge of honor. There were many drugs and good looking and well shaped girls. The honey pot was a fifty fifty chance. You could also get you head handed to you if you didn't watch your step. Many banditos who would cut your heart out for five dollars.

The six ILRP Marine Officers were dressed in Army khaki as privates. They played cards, drank a little until they found Baraja. For a few dollars the whores told them about Baraja. They hated him. He was an oral sex ferret. Baraja was playing cards with six men. An armed guard was in back of him. Kling, Pikus, and Wells watched him. Zeke, Eckert, and Sambach concentrated on the guard and other men paying attention to him. After one half hour Baraja stood up, looked around, then walked from the bar room to a hallway with the guard behind him. The hall way was dimmed. Baraja opened a door with the guard behind him who was pushed into the room by Kling, Pikus, and Wells. Pikus cold cocked the guard and Kling and Wells knocked out Baraja with their revolvers. A man and woman were counting money on a desk near the back exit from the room. Kling told Wells to get Eckert, Zeke, and Sambach to cover the window or outside back door. Pikus told the woman and man to get on the floor. He ripped out a wire from the wall then tied and gagged them. Kling tied and gagged the guard and Baraja. He took the box of money on the desk, went out to the bar and called to one of the whores. He told her to dividir (split) the money up with the girls. Quieto, silencio! (Quietly!) Zeke, Eckert, and Sambach dragged the tied guard and the two money counters out the back door about thirty feet from the building. With rope they found outside they tied all their legs together to a tree at a thirty-five degree angle. Kling, Pikus, and Wells searched the room. They found five revolvers, ammo, and a rifle as well as bags of marijuana and opio (opium). Baraja was coming back to life with a gash on his head bleeding. Kling wrapped the sleeves of a shirt he found to try and stop the bleeding, Pikus threw Baraja over his shoulder. The third building down the street was Baraja's warehouse, laboratory, and distribution center. Outside the building Colonel Peterson, three Army M.P. , and Detective Juan Torrio were waiting. They knocked the door down and entered the building. No one was working only two guards who gave up without a fight. Colonel Peterson called for Army trucks to unload the warehouse that was full of guns, bags of marijuana, and opio. Juan Torrio and Colonel Peterson said, "You people took a chance on Baraja being the big shot and cleaning up most of the problems in the U.S. Canal Zone." Colonel Kling said, "We can smell rats". Torrio said that most of the growing of cannabis and poppies was outside of the town of Florenica.

It was November 10, 1916 all the Marines were back on board the "Yo Misno" steamboat going through the Panama Canal. Detective Torrio was with them. Next stop Panama City, Torrio's hometown. So many dishonest government employees. Corruption of the highest officials. Everyone out for the money any way. Torrio said Florenica's cannabis and poppy fields were well guarded by government and civilians guards. Tough and mean. He believes we will need twenty-five men to do the job and get back to the "Yo Misno" in one piece. He had a map of the area. Roads were not good. Looks like a horse job for transportation. Some new vehicles were in Florenica - two trucks and one car closely both guarded.

Pikus said he was asking for volunteers from the boat's company and the Marines. There are twenty-eight of us on this boat. We are asking for twenty-four volunteers. This trip is going to be tough. It is do or die. If they catch you alive they will cut you up into little pieces and hang your flesh on the trees for the birds and vultures. No mercy! No problem with volunteers. Commander Kling, two sailors, and one Marine will stay on board. Captain Eckert and three Marines will hang out in the town of Florenica where the vehicles are parked ready to take over. If called each of his Marines will carry two hand grenades, revolvers, knife, and fifteen rounds of 38 cal. ammo. Captain Sambach and three Marines will steal twenty horses and have them in the bush in back of Detective Torrio's house. The two Navy corpsmen will stay on the boat. Major Zeke with one sailor and three Marines will take out the guards on Road -1- leading to the laboratory. On signal they will destroy the labs and out buildings and kill any opposition. Captain Sambach and his three Marines will take out the guards on Road -2- leading to the distribution center. Kill any opposition! Colonel Kling and four Marines will start fires and destroy any cannabis fields with chemicals and oil. Colonel Pikus with three Marines will destroy the poppy fields. Any opposition will be killed. Pick up any currency and weapons you can carry back. The horses will get you back the best way possible to the boat. Captain Eckert and his Marines will be the diversion in the town burning the vehicles and garage building. Commander Kling will be ready to leave port as soon as he believes he has everyone on board. The boat will be headed for Hoboken, New Jersey. Casualties - two Marines had arms cut. One Marine was shot in the left shoulder. Two Marines were shot in the left arm. Detective Torrio was happy and returned to his job at Panama City Police Department. He told his superiors he was shocked to hear what was happening while he was on vacation. Captain Sambach found one hundred thousand

American dollars. Colonel Kling called the twenty-eight men and asked for volunteers who could keep quiet on what was about to happen. All volunteered. Kling said it was about time a bonus was given out. To each sailor or Marine about 3,500 dollars. It was November 21, 1916 when the "Yo Misno" berthed at Hoboken, N.J. Commander Kling and Colonels Pikus and Kling stayed on the boat while the entire crew dressed in civilian clothes and went on shore to deposit or send their money home. The next day the three Officers sent their money home.

When all were on board Commander Kling said he had orders to take all hands to the Philadelphia Navy Yard. At the Navy Yard all hands were taken to the Naval Hospital Ward B 1 officers as well as the Navy and Marine crew. Two weeks observation, mental, and physical as well as some therapy. On December 7, 1916 all were released and assigned. The ILRP Officers were to report to their headquarters in Washington, D.C. and write out their reports. They were at their HQ for five days. It was December 14, 1916 when they were given furloughs to January 15, 1917 and told to report back to ILRP Headquarters. Their families were very happy to see them. Commander Kling and three crew members berthed the "Yo Misno" at the Philadelphia Navy Yard and then went on furlough.

Chapter 32

Installation Resources, Logistics Program
545 Independence Road
Washington, D.C.
January 15, 1917 1100 hours
Meeting: Subject 1 *Retirement of General John Smith
Commandant United States Marine Corps
January 1, 1892 to February 1, 1917.

Health reasons forced General Smith to retire effective February 2, 1917. General Smith served twenty-five years. He will temporarily be replaced by Lieutenant General John Barrows.

Subject II *ILRP Units will be disbanded February 1, 1917
Naval Marine Intelligence Department will replace the ILRP Units. Brigadier General John Dell Rico will command the new department. Colonel Lew Byrne will serve as second in command. All Officers and enlisted personnel who want to transfer to the new department are eligible. They may also transfer to other units.

Qualifications for Military Personnel to Naval Marine Intelligence Department:

1. Three years military experience.
2. Attended language school or foreign embassy - 6 months.
3. Communication skills telegraph, signal flags, telephone.
4. Weapons qualifications - rifle and pistol marksman.
5. Fitness report - health.
6. Eye sight - at least 20 - 30 both eyes. Age limit 18 - 32.
7. Height 5'8" to 6'4".
8. Weight 160 - 190.
9. No record of venereal diseases.
10. High school or military school graduate. Previous two years military experience of command oral testing - written testing.

100% of the Marines in the ILRP Unit qualified.

The new department was formed. Headquarters and offices were at the same location. Changes were in local and foreign security. Protecting the United States and its territories from terrorist attacks, espionage, sabotage, traitors, and treason. One month schooling on assignments.

Unit 1	Unit 2	Unit 3
Colonel Kling	Colonel Pikus	Captain Eckert
Major Zeke	Major Wells	Captain Sambach
24 trained agents	24 trained agents	24 trained agents

Assignment at and for the United States and its Possessions
District of Colombia
America Samoa   Commonwealth of Puerto Rico
Guam Virgin Island St. Croix
Navasso St. John - St. Thomas
Wake Island Wake Atoll
Midway Island
Midway Atoll
On April 6, 1917 the United States declared war on Germany.

On April 12, 1917 on the South Pier on the Jersey City waterfront the Colombia, a transport supply ship was taking on wood boxes and merchandise for export to England. It was 12:15 pm when an explosion occurred on the ship and pier fire quickly spread like someone put oil or inflammable material on the pier. The local fire department appeared and with the help of the pier fire crew extinguished the fire. Many heavy wooden boxes were burnt and broken. Exposed were rifles, pistols, and gun parts. On the ship in number one hole explosion after explosions. Ammunition and grenades were going off. Explosions in hold number one on the ship went off for one half hour. Other sections of the ship were damaged. It took two days for the local New Jersey, New York Police and some Federal investigators to check out the fires. Their findings were sabotage by persons unknown. The acting Commandant of the Marine Corp was asked for help because he had experienced officers who were now in the Naval Marine Intelligence Dept. Other Federal Departments backed up the request. The new Commandant of the Marines said for all agencies to contact General Dell Rico who was in charge of the new department. General Dell Rico called together Colonels

201

Kling and Pikus, Majors Zeke and Wells, and Captains Eckert and Sambach. They were all old friends. They were ready to go to work. Identification cards and government badges were passed out, also, choice of handguns. Colonel Kling's right arm was giving him trouble so Colonel Pikus took over the ship and pier explosion and fire investigation. He dispatched Captain Eckert to pick up reports from the Jersey City and New York Police Departments on the explosion and fire also, any pictures or information on suspects. Captain Sambach was to check on the stevedores or other people who were in the area. Major Wells was to check the Colombia's ship crew and Captain on any troublesome or foreign crew members. Major Zeke was to check bars, whorehouses, or anywhere crew or pier workers would hang out. Union organizers were in the area. Headquarters was the Brooklyn Navy Yard.

In the rear of the Marine Barracks was a private entrance, three rooms, two for sleeping and a large office. Major Bryla an old friend was in charge of the Marine Guard, one hundred strong. The NMID Officers could eat their meals when they were in quarters with Major Bryla and his officers. They had their uniforms with them but were to dress in civilian clothes. Two Ford cars were available. The Marine officers, Sergeants of the Guard, and Gate Guards were instructed on the NMID identification cards and badges out on these plain clothes men. No saluting. About twenty of the older Sergeants and Marines served with Kling and Pikus in the Caribbean Islands and the Philippines. Colonel Kling had one long conference type table, three desks, ten office chairs, and three metal lock files in the large office, as well as three telephones. The telephone telegraph room for communications was in the Marine Barracks. Most messages were in code. The five officers brought in information for Colonel Kling to look over. Colonel Pikus was called to Washington for instructions. Kling looked over the information and pictures. One picture showed four men on the pier looking at the fire. That interested Kling. The old story that criminals sometimes come back to see their crime was sometimes proven to be true. Kling had seven copies made and gave each one of his officers a copy. He said, "Marines get me a complete background on each of these men." It took two weeks. Three of the men checked out. One man could not be identified. The other men on the pier thought he was a stevedore. You could depend on Major Wells. Old whorehouses Wells got the information on the fourth man. He was a monthly customer. His name was Kurt Goring and he lived at 789 East 91st Street in Manhattan in a four family brown stone. He told Ann and Linda his favorite whores how much he liked them. He took them out for dinner once in a while. What puzzled the girls was he always had a lot of money and never worked. Ann said customers like Kurt could make them millionaires. He was good with a buck but bad with a two girl _____. Both girls were good fakers. Kling said that when Colonel Pikus came back from Washington they would check out Goring's residence.

It was February 5, 1917 Colonel Pikus was back the night before and he was still sleeping at 0600 hours. Colonel Kling told the officers he planned a meeting for 1500 hours. It was now 1000 hours. He told Wells to get the officers and they would drive up and take a look at 789 East 91st Street. "Let's look at the entrance, exits, window, roof, and for a garage." On the return trip to their office Eckert said it looked like a lot of wires were on the roof. Maybe an antenna? "I bet this building has a Morse telegraph." Back at headquarters Pikus said, "Let's keep this Kurt Goring under surveillance for a few days. Eckert and Zeke first eight hour watch. Take one car. Telephone in if possible every two hours." While they were all together Kling passed out money for expenses. He said, "Watch yourselves, move around, do not park in one place too long. Look out for local police. They can be a pain in the ass sometimes."

After one week of surveillance on Kurt Goring nothing occurred other than his visit to his whores and eating out. The Captain of the Colombia telephoned Colonel Pikus and said his two cooks were missing. They were out on five hours liberty and never came back. That was Tuesday. Today is

Thursday. Their clothes and belongings are still here. It appears they were coming back. Major Bryla telephoned the NMID Office and said two New York Detectives wanted to see Colonel Kling. Kling said, "I will be right over to your office." Kling had talked to these two detectives before, Detectives Smith and York. York was the senior man. He told Kling the two stevedores found in the ships hole and the one on the pier died. They were talking about the two missing cooks from the Colombia when the Duty Sergeant ushered in two Jersey City Detectives. After the greetings Detectives Grubowski and Jones said that this morning at low tide at Pier Four two white males were found tied back to back by their necks, feet, and arms to a log piling that could only be seen at low tide. A fisherman spotted them. Kling said to call the Captain from the Colombia. We forgot to check the ship's registry. The Captain from the Colombia identified the bodies as his cooks. The Colombia was registered in Argentina. The two dead cooks names were Otto Fraunhofer and Ernst Haeckel, both former German Seaman. They were both hired out of the Argentina Seaman's Hall. Their records indicated they had lived in Argentina for five years and were citizens. The Colombia's Captain said they were good cooks and appeared good deck hands. No trouble with them. Both had said they were not married. After the bodies were identified Kling and Pikus accompanied the Colombia's Captain back to his ship. They asked to check records of the crew. The Captain could object but he didn't. The Captain said, "Three days before they left Mar del Plata the police came around checking the pier. They had asked the Captain if he saw anything unusual brought on the ship by the crew members or officers. They told the ship's Captain parties unknown stole dynamite, fuses, and caps from a large construction company. The company was about two miles from the port. Kling asked the Captain who had the gang plank watch the three days they were in port. One seaman who had the watch on the day before they left said Ernst came back on board from leave with two suitcases, one large one and a small one. Ernst told the seaman the suitcases had new clothes in them. The seaman who's name was Juan and who spoke broken English thought nothing of this. The suitcases were found and turned over to the Jersey City Police. After further questioning of the officers and crew Pikus and Kling returned to their headquarters.

On April 30, 1917 the Jersey City Police laboratory telephoned Colonel Kling. The Sergeant in Charge, Sgt. Brooks said that a small piece of fuse and some residue was found in the small suitcase of Ernst Haeckel. Kling said, "Marines we are going on surveillance again." Kling and Zeke were the first two to go on night surveillance not far from 789 East 91st Street. It was May 1, 1917. At 0900 hours two men entered the front entrance of 789 East 91st St. Fifteen minutes later three more men entered the front entrance. Kling stayed on surveillance while Zeke located a telephone to tell Pikus to bring Wells, Eckert, Sambach, and six civilian clothed Marines well armed to 789 East 91st Street. Kling was waiting two doors away. When they arrived Kling assigned Wells and three Marines to the rear of the building, three Marines to climb the fire escape to the roof and to stop anyone up there. Kling, Zeke, Eckert, Sambach, and Pikus well armed broke down the front door with axes and rushed in. On the first floor they found two well lit furnished apartments. No one was there. On the second floor men tried to get out the roof door and two of them were cold cocked by Marine rifle butts. Two went out a rear window on the second floor. Pikus worked them over. Kurt Goring and the other man gave themselves up. Explosives and handguns were found in one room. The New York City Police were called. All the suspects were taken to Army Headquarters at Governors' Island, New York for interrogation, all six men were spies. Kurt Goring was the leader. They were indicted and convicted of espionage, sabotage, and murder. All were found guilty and executed. Police never found out anything about Kurt Goring or how he got into the country.

Colonel Kling took a chance raiding 789 East 91st Street with his Marines. He knew in his heart that this was the spies' headquarters. Information found at that address helped to pick up twenty German spies on the East Coast of the United States.

Nine Marines; General Smith, General Dell Rico, Colonel Byrnes, Colonels Kling and Pikus, Majors Wells and Zeke, and Captains Eckert and Sambach were the forerunners of the FBI and Secret Service.

Chapter 33

The new department set up by the U.S. Navy, Naval Marine Intelligence Corps is Commanded by General John Dell Rico and Colonel Lew Byrnes. It was formed and started action immediately. United States now at war serious problems no doubt will flare up at home, possessions, and protectorates. The six agents Colonels Pikus and Kling, Majors Wells and Zeke, and Captains Sambach and Eckert requested combat duty with the 5th and 8th Marine regiments getting ready to depart for France. All requests were denied on the grounds that they were needed and valuable to the corps and country for security of possessions and protectorates. Trouble started again all over the Caribbean, West Indies, and South Atlantic. Reports without enough confirmation stated German raiders and submarines were sighted off Antigua which is a United Kingdom possession.

New recruits, Marines, and Navy personnel wanted to get into the fight in Europe. They were not interested in home and possession security. Fifty service personnel applied to the NMID Dept. Only ten Marines and two Navy men qualified. Marines were rushed to St. Croix a U.S. possession in the Caribbean. The Germans wanted the island for a submarine base. In the Pacific the Germans were trying to get a cruiser into Guam Harbor.

General Dell Rico called for a meeting at NMID Headquarters in Washington D.C. He ordered the following to attend: Commander Frank E. Kling USCG, Lt. Commander Louie Byrnes USN, and Lieutenant Bruce Jones USN, also Colonels Kling and Pikus, Captains Eckert and Sambach. The meeting was scheduled for two days. Your present duties are re-assigned. May 26 & 27, 1917 - 0900 hours to 1400 hours. Civilian dress, no uniforms. The new NMID Headquarters was at the same headquarters used by the ILRP. Sleeping quarters and food available.

President Edson was up in arms. He was having trouble with the Senate and House of Representatives on how the war should be directed. The goof balls in the Navy Department wanted to send battle wagons and battleships to the Caribbean and South Atlantic on the submarine scare. Commander Frank E. Kling one of the few Navy officers who studies were on submarines while he was on convoy duty to England spoke out. On overlay stays waiting to return to the United States Commander Kling attended the British Submarine School at Plymouth and Liverpool. He was inside of British and German submarines. He saw the potential of submarine warfare. What submarine warfare could do to a Navy who did not believe a submarine could destroy Navy battle and merchant ships. His reports he turned in to the Navy Department caught Secretary Daniels' eye. Daniels believed in Kling and ordered twelve 172 x 23 - 01.3 FF submarine chasers built. That was six months before the United States was at war.

The subchasers built of wood, reinforced hulls 2XM Hoovein Owen Rentschler diesel engine, two stroke cycles, speed 29 knots, large batteries, single screw, plus Naval equipment for that size boat. It also will have a crew of fifty-seven men. The boat was armed with four depth bombs and 1.5 50 cal. gun, one two pounder, and four 30 cal. Lewis guns. Small arms, forty 30 cal. Springfield rifles, twenty-five 38 cal. pistols, twenty-four hand grenades, and flares. The new Destroyer Richey will be the command ship because of Commander Kling's experience of water depths, port locations, anchorage of large and small ships, knowledge of Navel and Military problems. Secretary Daniels asked Commander Kling if he would take the responsibility of Navel, Military, and, shipping in the designated areas of the South Atlantic Ocean and Caribbean Sea. Kling's flotilla would be eight subchasers and the Destroyer Richey. Daniels knew "Kling would take the command without being ordered."

The new Destroyer Richey was 376 feet in length and had a 40 foot beam, a battery of six 5 inch 38 cal. guns, and smaller calibre guns made up the boats armmament for hostile action. Eight subchasers and the Destroyer Richey were to assemble outside of the ship yard and Port Charleston, S.C.

June 26th 1917 at 1200 hours for a shake down cruise. All boats had trained crews and equipment. Commander Kling was promoted to Captain and given All in Command of the Flotilla. Commander Louie Byrnes was in command of SC #'s 40, 41, 42, and 43. Lt. Commander Bruce Jones was in command of SC #'s 44, 45, 46, and 47. Before the shake down cruises boat Captains attended a meeting for instructions and given orders at the Charleston Port Authority Building.

Commander Louie Byrnes' command subchaser #40 and subchasers #'s 41, 42, and 43 will leave Port Charleston June 27, 1917 at 1300 hours. Byrnes' Flotilla will travel south pass Miami, Key West, through the Straits of Florida into the Gulf of Mexico around Cuba, Greater Antilles in the Caribbean Sea where the flotilla would meet the fuel and supply ship Wright near Montego Bay, Jamaica. After fueling and supplies the ship will travel to the Mayaguez ship yard Puerto Rico. The repair ship Conrad is standing by at Swan Island if any help is needed. All repairs will be made at the Mayaguez ship yard. All boats will remain at Port Mayaguez. Lt. Commander Jones' command subchaser #44 and SC #45 will leave Port Charleston June 28, 1917 at 0900 hours and travel south pass the Bahama Islands to San Juan shipyard in Puerto Rico. The repair ship Paramount is at the San Juan ship yard if help is needed. The USS Richey with Captain Kling in command with subchasers #46 and 47 will leave Port Charleston on June 30, 1917 and travel north then east to Bermuda. After refueling the Richey and SC #'s 46 and 47 will travel south to San Juan, Puerto Rico. All subchaser command boats are to report daily on speed and diesel engine problems, also any other problems before reaching their destinations.

After leaving Bermuda traveling south the USS Richey radio room orderly gave Captain Kling a communication from the Merchant Ship Eileen 1 traveling from Cartagena, Colombia with coffee to Cork Ireland. The ship was traveling northeast. The ship's Captain reported seeing at a distance two submarines also traveling northeast. They were forty miles northeast of St. Thomas and traveling to fuel. First stop the Azores Islands. Captain Kling's boat the Richey and SC #'s 46 and 47 dispersed within sighting distance of each other traveling on a course they thought may intercept the submarines. No contact was made with the unidentified submarines. Kling's message to the Irish Captain of the Eileen 1 was, "Did you forget that a sea war was on?" He told the Captain if he reached the Azure Islands to get into a convoy to England. The ship Eileen 1 could suffer a coup de main and end up coup de grace. Kling said to be careful and keep a twenty-four hour double watch. A German ship was reported in the lanes you are traveling. A German raider ship looks like any neutral merchant ship flying a foreign flag. When the ship gets within a range of any merchant ships guns come out from nowhere to fire and sink any merchant ships giving aid to the German enemies. Captain Kling liked the Irish people. He was in Ireland a few times and liked the Irish made stew and lassies. His grandmother was born in Killarney.

The USS Richey and subchasers #46 and #47 got back on course to San Juan, Puerto Rico. When Captain Kling's small flotilla was eight nautical miles away from the Island of Anegada a message came in to the radio room of the Richey that an unidentified submarine was sighted near Vieques Island traveling south. This was reported by a large island to island trade wind jammer. Captain Kling and the eight subchasers in his command all on a shake down cruise traversed the Caribbean Sea and areas indicated by the Navy Dept. No signs of German submarines or German raiders were located.

All the subchasers were assigned areas. The Richey returned to Norfolk ship yard for reassignment. Captain Kling was ordered to the Navy Department Washington D.C. On a second request for combat duty Colonels Kling and Pikus, Majors Zeke and Wells, and Captains Eckert and Sambach went to France with the 6th and 8th Marines.